# EAT YOUR WORDS

### 125 Food & Beverage Themed
### Puzzles for Hungry Minds

## LISA
## PATRIN

# Dedication

This book is dedicated to my husband John and to my children, Joshua, and Nicholas, who have always enthusiastically supported my culinary journey. It has been and will always be one of life's greatest pleasures to cook for and dine with them. To my Dad who led by example and taught me that I can do anything if I set my mind to it, no matter how difficult and to my Mom, my Grandma Dolores and the Slick and Delmonico families, who taught me that one of the finest ways to connect and nurture is through food. It will forever be my love language.

# Introduction

I created the Eat Your Words puzzle book to satisfy our voracious appetite for culinary knowledge and to nurture the curiosity for all things delicious in a fun and interesting way. This book contains 125 puzzles related to food, beverages and cooking. Whether there is one word in the answer, or more, be assured they will all fit correctly into the answer boxes without spaces.

Spend the morning sipping coffee and puzzling, keep this book in your briefcase and work the puzzles over lunch, or pack it into a carry-on for your next trip and learn on the go.

"Learn Well, Eat Well, Live Well"

# Contents

# 1

# Sausage

1. Spicy, smooth Cajun flavored sausage. Often used in recipes such as jambalaya.
2. Produced from pork and occasionally veal. Comes in a variety of flavors, including beer and cheese. Name is German in origin.
3. Pork sausage flavored with garlic and fennel seed. Varieties include both hot and mild. Can be bought in bulk or link form.
4. Smoked Polish sausages made with beef and pork and generously seasoned with garlic, pimento, and cloves.
5. Spicy, hard sausage made with pork and beef. Often used to top pizza.

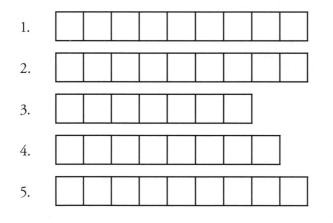

Answers on page 127

# 2

# Squash

1. Dimpled, hard flesh. Ranges from green to bright orange. Yields the best flavor when baked or boiled and mashed.
2. A winter squash that is sometimes called a Japanese pumpkin. Outer skin is deep green, flesh is orange. Naturally, sweet flavor. Can be used in place of pumpkin or buttercup squash.
3. Smooth and pale green, with a bottle-gourd shape and hollow interior chambers. Frequently used in Chinese recipes, stir fries or soups. Exterior is sometimes used to make bowls and maracas.
4. A winter squash that is readily available in the Midwest. Frequently halved, seeded and baked with butter and brown sugar. Usually weighs from 1 to 3 pounds.
5. Also called a peanut squash due to its shape. About 6 inches long and green to gold with a striped appearance. Has a creamy pulp that tastes similar to a sweet potato.

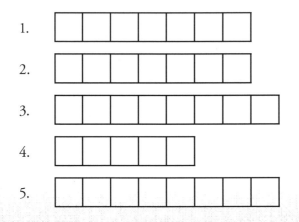

Answers on page 127

# 3

# Nuts

1. Exotic nut with a coconut-like flavor. About 1 inch in diameter; light in color. Originated in Australia but also cultivated in Hawaii and Central America.
2. Known for its distinctive, full flavor and characteristic green color. Shells are very hard and sometimes dyed a red color. Often purchased in the shell.
3. Small and oval in shape; ivory in color. Often found in Italian dishes. Key ingredient in pesto.
4. Frequently used in meat and poultry stuffing. High starch content, which makes it a good choice for mashing. Can be roasted and sliced. Good addition to salads or stir-fry dishes.
5. Popular snacking nut. Often found on the appetizer table. Has a sweet, buttery flavor. Never sold in the shell as both inner and outer shell coverings contain a toxic, caustic oil.

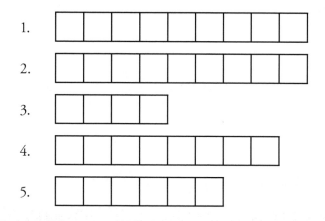

1. ☐☐☐☐☐☐☐☐☐
2. ☐☐☐☐☐☐☐☐☐☐
3. ☐☐☐☐
4. ☐☐☐☐☐☐☐☐
5. ☐☐☐☐☐☐

Answers on page 127

# 4

# Sauces

1. A complex emulsified sauce made of butter and egg yolks. Commonly flavored with fresh tarragon and chopped shallots.
2. White sauce found frequently in French cuisine. Often used as a base for more complex sauces. Produced by whisking scalded milk into a roux of melted butter and flour.
3. French sauce with a brownish color, named for the wines of Bordeaux. The combination of wine, beef marrow and shallots give this a rich, distinctive flavor.
4. Flavorful emulsion commonly made of eggs, garlic, lemon juice and oil. Considered a light, mayonnaise-style sauce. Mustard is an optional addition.
5. Prepared by combining a roux of flour and butter with a rich stock instead of scalded milk. Frequently used as a topping for poultry and seafood dishes.

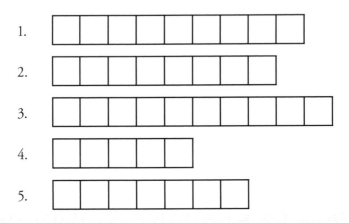

Answers on page 127

# 5

# Sugar

1. Granulated sugar ground to a smooth powder, then sifted. Contains a small amount of cornstarch to prevent sticking or caking.
2. Large crystal sugar used primarily in the baking and candy industries as an edible decoration, giving a glittering or sparkling look. It does not dissolve when exposed to heat.
3. Raw sugar that is only partially processed, so it has a blond color. Flavor is mild and delicate. Often used as a sweetener in tea or other beverages.
4. Unrefined British specialty brown sugar with a dark brown color and a strong molasses flavor. Texture of the crystals is stickier and coarser than standard brown sugar.
5. A washed, raw-cane specialty sugar crystallized from pressing. It is delicate, crunchy, and light brown in color. Name originates from a colony in Guyana where the sugar was originally produced in large quantities.

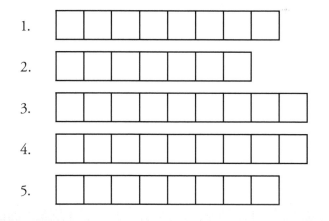

Answers on page 127

# 6

# Flour

1. Almost all pastas are made of this coarsely ground durum wheat flour. Has a much higher gluten content than all-purpose flour.
2. Soft, fine textured. Low-gluten flour with a high starch content. Often used in quick breads and pie crusts. Available in both bleached and unbleached varieties.
3. Unbleached, high-gluten flour that adds elasticity to dough for baking, allowing it to hold its shape. Malted barley is added to increase yeast activity.
4. Used primarily for making gravies and sauces. Cannot be substituted for all-purpose flour. Dissolves quickly in liquid. This is a specialty flour.
5. High protein and fat content. Made from lightly toasted or raw beans that are ground into a fine powder. Contains no gluten. Adds tenderness and moisture to baked goods.

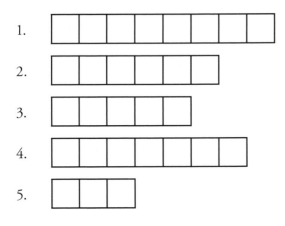

Answers on page 127

# 7

# Stone Fruits

1. First cultivated in China 4000 years ago. About 90 percent of the American crop comes from California. Varieties include Royal and Tilton. Skin colors range from pale yellow to deep orange.
2. Falls into two categories: freestone, where the pit falls out easily when the fruit is split, and clingstone, where the pit "clings" to the fruit.
3. Dates to 300 B.C. Named after the Turkish town of Cerasus. Fruit trees presented to America's capital by Tokyo's Governor in 1912.
4. The skin has a broad range of colors, from shades of yellow to dark purple or even indigo blue. Size is one to three inches in diameter. Very juicy.
5. Skin is shiny, smooth and has no fuzz, which distinguishes it from another stone fruit. Name means sweet as nectar.

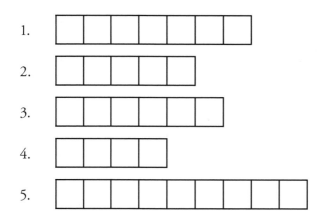

Answers on page 127

# 8

# Olives

1. Spanish in origin. Green in color and often stuffed with pimento or garlic. Frequent garnish in martinis or bloody Mary's.
2. Greek in origin. Ranges in color from black to deep purple. Rich and nutty flavor. Often found in Italian or Mediterranean dishes.
3. Tiny, oval shape. Harvested when fully ripe. Purple to brown-black. Cured and packed in olive oil. A key ingredient in a popular French salad.
4. Common black olive, larger in size. Lacks the flavor and character of most European olives. Often found on salad bars and is frequently used as a pizza topping.
5. Method of soaking olives and other food in a liquid solution often containing water, sugar, salt and occasionally herbs and spices.

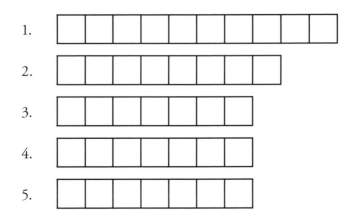

Answers on page 127

# 9

# Taste of Japan

1. Slightly sweet wine made of steamed, fermented rice.
2. Skillfully prepared dish made by rolling rice, seafood, or other ingredients into a sheet of seaweed. It is cut it into smaller pieces prior to serving.
3. Thick noodles made from wheat and flour. Can be purchased fresh or dried in Asian markets.
4. Vegetables or seafood deep-fried in a light batter. Has a light puffy coating and a crunchy texture.
5. Omelet seasoned and filled with fried rice. Originated in Tokyo.

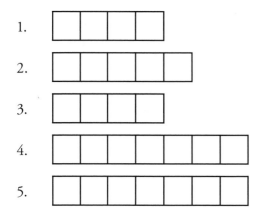

Answers on page 127

# 10

# Mushrooms

1. Yellow to orange in color. Funnel or trumpet-like shape. Fruity, apricot fragrance and peppery taste. Often used in French cooking; prized by chefs.
2. Chocolate brown color. Frequently dried, preserved and packaged. Often used in Japanese and Chinese cooking.
3. Gray, with a shape like a seashell. Grows in layers on deciduous wood and has virtually no stem. Often used in stir-fried dishes.
4. Gray to brown. Flesh is sponge-like. One of the best flavored mushrooms, has a nutty taste. Usually, one to six inches in height and grows in abundance after a forest fire. Much sought after by wild mushroom foragers.
5. Has a long growing cycle and can reach six inches in diameter. The mature relative of the cremini mushroom. Dark brown in color with a meaty flavor.

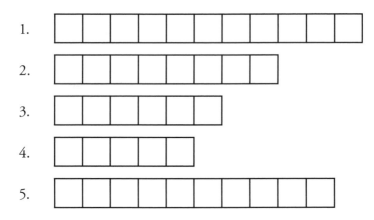

Answers on page 127

# 11

# Taste of Mexico

1. Pork dish from Sinaloa prepared by simmering for a long time, then frying in a spicy chile sauce. Used as a filling for tacos or fajitas.
2. Two tortillas with filling between, cooked on both sides until golden.
3. Name means the painted bean. Known for its characteristic brown, mottled skin. Essential ingredient in many Mexican dishes, often eaten refried.
4. Extremely popular dish. Fillings are wrapped within a tortilla, which is topped with a chile or mole sauce and baked.
5. Flavorful combination of fresh ingredients, including chopped tomatoes, onions, chiles and spices.

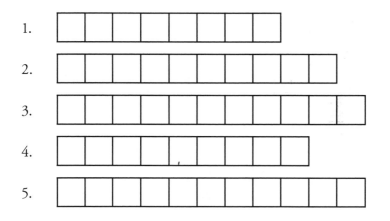

1. ☐☐☐☐☐☐☐
2. ☐☐☐☐☐☐☐☐☐
3. ☐☐☐☐☐☐☐☐☐☐☐
4. ☐☐☐☐☐,☐☐☐☐
5. ☐☐☐☐☐☐☐☐☐☐

Answers on page 127

# 12

# Hungarian Cuisine

1.  A well-known dish made of beef, onions, and spices.
2.  An alcoholic drink distilled from fruit grown on the Hungarian plains. Comes in several flavors including apricot, cherry and plum.
3.  A pastry made of layers that include either poppy seed, apple, cherry, cheese, or curd.
4.  Spice made from grinding sweet red peppers that have been dried. Adds vibrant color and flavor that ranges from mild to sweet.
5.  Sponge cake layered with rich, chocolate cream and a coating of crunchy caramel bits. Said to have been invented by the famous Hungarian confectioner Jozsef C. Dobos in 1884.

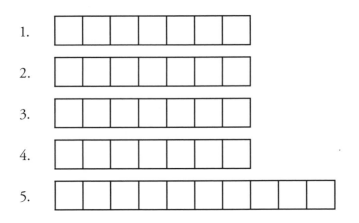

Answers on page 127

# 13

# Taste of Sicily

1. A zesty salad made with eggplant, olives, capers, and celery.
2. A dessert made of fried tubular pastry shells filled with ricotta and additional flavorings.
3. Name given to all Italian cheeses made from sheep's milk. Most of these are hard, dry cheeses good for grating and using in cooking.
4. A kind of ice cream, said to have been invented in Sicily during Roman times, when a relay of runners would bring snow down from Mount Etna to be flavored and served to wealthy patricians.
5. A dessert wine often used as a cooking ingredient.

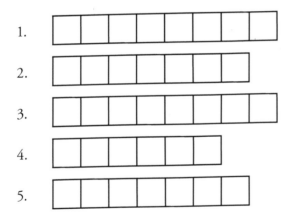

Answers on page 127

# 14

# Tropical Fruits

1. A South American fruit shaped like a pinecone. Gray or green in color with a scaly pattern. Pulp is cream-colored and has a soft texture. The black seeds are not edible. The flavor is a combination of pineapple, papaya, and banana.

2. Sweet, fragrant fruit grown in South America, as well as California, Hawaii, and Florida. The whole fruit is edible but should be very ripe when eaten raw. The skin ranges from yellow to red or purplish black. The flesh can be pale yellow to red. Frequently used in jams and sauces.

3. Largest tree fruit in the world, as much as 100 pounds in weight. Grows in Africa, Brazil, and Southeast Asia. Shape is oblong or oval. Can only be purchased canned in the United States. Yellowish pulp that tastes like banana.

4. Looks like a large green banana and is typically cooked prior to eating. Used like potatoes in both Hispanic and Caribbean cooking.

5. Very aromatic fruit with a tart flavor. Grows on a climbing vine. Color is yellow to dark purple when mature. Often used to produce juice.

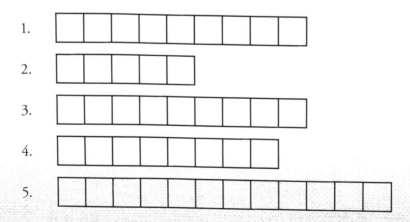

Answers on page 127

# 15

# French Terms

1. A small bite before the meal begins; means "to amuse the mouth".
2. Phrase meaning "I wish you a hearty appetite" or "enjoy your meal".
3. Drink served with a light appetizer before a large meal.
4. Bread made from a rich yeast dough containing large amounts of eggs and butter. Formed into a roll or bun or baked into a special mold.
5. A dish topped with butter and breadcrumbs or cheese prior to placing it under the broiler until it becomes crisp or golden in color.

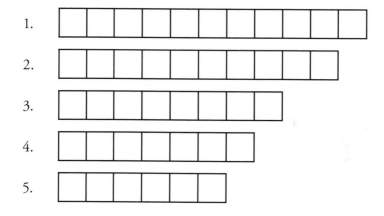

Answers on page 127

# 16

# Mangoes

1. In what country is the mango tree considered sacred?
2. The succulent flesh of the mango is what bright and vibrant color?
3. Fresh mangoes are rich in Vitamin C and what other vitamin?
4. Spice that is made from ground, unripe mangoes.
5. Variety of mango that is dominant in production.

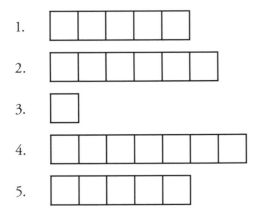

Answers on page 127

# 17

# Citrus

1. This vitamin C-packed fruit makes up three-quarters of the citrus world market. Said to have originated in China.
2. One of the most acidic of all citrus fruits. Grows well in tropical areas where lemons do not. Green, though skin turns pale yellow at full ripeness.
3. Bite-sized fruit that can be eaten whole with the rind. Flavor is tart. Ranges from yellow to red.
4. Grown primarily in Italy. Oil from the rind has a floral scent. Mainly used in perfumes and Earl Grey tea.
5. Rind of this small yellowish-orange fruit is used to flavor some foods as well as vinegars and preserves. Looks somewhat like a very small grapefruit, with yellow to green skin and an uneven texture.

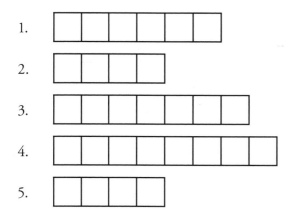

Answers on page 127

# 18

# Taste of China

1. Famous duck dish said to have originated in Beijing. Called a national food of China. Derives its unique taste from the seasonings and crispy skin.
2. Type of rice porridge eaten in China and many other Asian countries.
3. Dumpling frequently used in Chinese cuisine. It consists of very thin pastry made of wheat flour, salt, and water. This is usually filled with flavorful meat or vegetarian ingredients.
4. Traditional Chinese meal that involves many light side dishes served with tea. These items are typically served in steamer baskets and diners choose which items they would like.
5. Chinese "fondue" in which ingredients are cooked in a large communal metal pot with simmering stock.

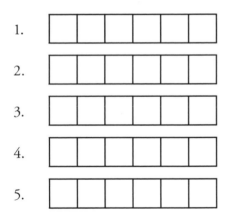

1. ▢▢▢▢▢▢

2. ▢▢▢▢▢▢

3. ▢▢▢▢▢▢

4. ▢▢▢▢▢▢

5. ▢▢▢▢▢▢

Answers on page 127

# 19

# Taste of Australia

1. A traditional Australian outback soda bread that is made without yeast. It is cooked over the fire in a cast iron skillet or directly over the coals of an open fire.
2. Dessert named after a famous ballerina. It is made of sugar and egg white meringue. It's topped with whipped cream and fresh fruit before serving.
3. An animal hunted in the wild, but not farmed.
4. Freshwater crayfish found in the temperate region of Australia.
5. This black, salty spread is a yeast extract that is popular for use on sandwiches.

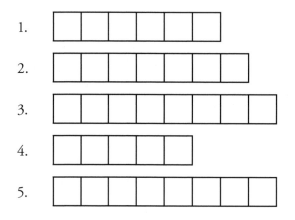

1.
2.
3.
4.
5.

Answers on page 127

# 20

# World of Dumplings

1. Name of this traditional Italian dumpling means "lump". Can be used in place of noodles in soups or stews. The ingredients may include flour, potatoes, or farina. Eggs or cheese can be added to the dough as well as finely chopped spinach.
2. Polish specialty, either sweet or savory, that is half-moon shaped. Made with unleavened dough that can be stuffed with ingredients such as cabbage, sauerkraut, or onions.
3. In German, the name means "little sparrow". These tiny dumplings are prepared with a mixture of flour, eggs, water or milk, salt and occasionally nutmeg. Generally boiled, then added to soups or stews. Also, can be tossed in butter or served as a side dish similar to rice or potatoes.
4. Dumplings made with won-ton skins, usually filled with ground meat, pork, or seafood.
5. Korean dumplings that contain kimchi, ground pork, vegetables, or cellophane noodles. Can be fried, steamed, or boiled.

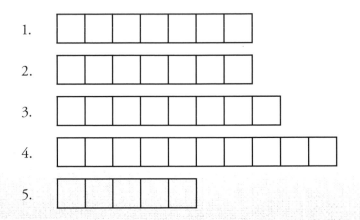

Answers on page 127

# 21

# Taste of Greece

1. Well-known curd cheese that is salted and cured in a brine solution. Usually made from sheep or goat's milk. Popular addition the traditional Greek salad.
2. Layered baked dish, consists of ground meat, tomatoes, pasta, and a variety of spices. It is topped with bechamel sauce. Frequently finished with a light dusting of cinnamon or nutmeg.
3. Sweet dessert created by layering a combination of phyllo dough, nuts, sugar, syrup, honey, and cloves. Traditionally cut into small diamond shapes.
4. Popular anise-flavored liqueur that is widely recognized and consumed throughout Greece. Usually served as an aperitif or with small plates of food.
5. Greek appetizer made of cheese that is most often fried. Served with a sprinkling of lemon juice and chopped parsley.

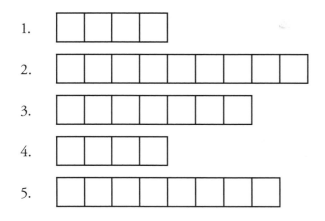

1. ☐☐☐☐
2. ☐☐☐☐☐☐☐☐☐
3. ☐☐☐☐☐☐☐
4. ☐☐☐☐
5. ☐☐☐☐☐☐☐☐

Answers on page 127

# 22

# Tea

1.  Indian in origin. This black tea has a rich, malt-like flavor.
2.  Traditional Chinese tea. Bronze in color, with flavor of almonds.
3.  One of the most popular and well-known tea varieties. Blend of China black and Darjeeling and flavored with oil of bergamot.
4.  Made from green tea leaves scented with a specific white flower.
5.  Has an opaque, tan color that results from milk added as a creamer. Its flavor comes from the many spices that can be added, including cloves, cinnamon, ginger and more. Sometimes referred to as spiced milk tea.

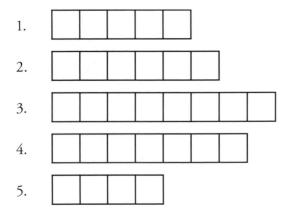

Answers on page 127

# 23

# Taste of Germany

1. Tiny dumplings that are tossed with butter or added to other dishes, such as soup.
2. Highly seasoned German stew made with marinated rabbit.
3. Shredded cabbage, salted and fermented in its own juices.
4. Beef roast marinated in a sour-sweet mixture.
5. A liqueur with flavors of bitter herbs, cola, and chocolate.

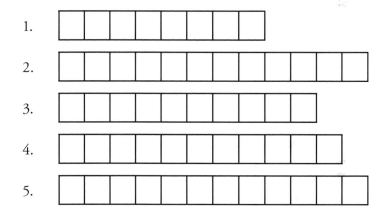

1. ☐☐☐☐☐☐☐☐

2. ☐☐☐☐☐☐☐☐☐☐☐☐

3. ☐☐☐☐☐☐☐☐☐☐☐

4. ☐☐☐☐☐☐☐☐☐☐☐

5. ☐☐☐☐☐☐☐☐☐☐☐☐

Answers on page 127

# 24

# Let's Talk Turkey

1.  Name for the adult male turkey, which is larger and more brightly colored than the female and can weigh as much as 30 pounds.
2.  Name for the adult female turkey, which usually weighs 8 to 10 pounds.
3.  Part of the turkey's stomach that contains tiny stones to help grind up their food.
4.  Cluster of long feathers resembling hair on the chests of male turkeys. Hint: Santa has a white one.
5.  Part of turkey that is dried and tugged by two people to bring good luck. Originated from the English custom of merry thought, which means the person holding the longer half of it will be the next to marry.

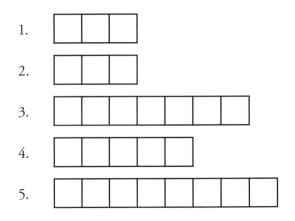

Answers on page 127

# 25

# Pumpkins

1. Pumpkins are made up of 90% what?
2. Pumpkins are used to make these seasonal fall desserts. Hint: they are traditionally served at Thanksgiving.
3. High in Vitamin A and another mineral.
4. Once recommended for removing what common skin markings?
5. Contains high levels of what antioxidant?

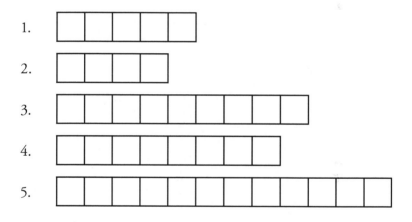

Answers on page 127

# 26

# Taste of Morocco

1. Name refers to both this flavorful Moroccan stew and the clay pot in which it is cooked.
2. The tiny semolina grains of this dish must be cooked in liquid and stirred carefully to break up any clumps.
3. This tender lamb dish can be slow cooked in the oven but is often cooked in an earthenware container. Name means "roasted in an open fire".
4. Traditional pie that can have either savory or sweet flavors, typically has three layers and is wrapped in a thin pastry.
5. This sweet tasting dessert has the consistency of a custard dish. It is flavored with orange flower water and garnished with almonds and ground cinnamon.

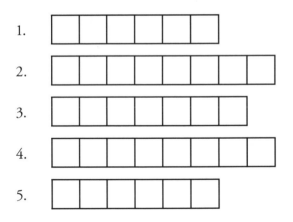

Answers on page 127

# 27

# Taste of Nicaragua

1. Spanish for "little cheese". A piece of cheese is rolled inside a tortilla along with pickled onions, cream, and a pinch of salt.
2. Dessert prepared with condensed milk, milk, and cream. Name officially means "three milks". A cake is prepared, then the milk mixture is added after baking.
3. Mixture of fried rice, onions, sweet peppers, and red beans that are boiled with garlic.
4. Tomato-based chile salsa used as a dip or sauce for many Nicaraguan meals.
5. A green banana, also known as a plantain.

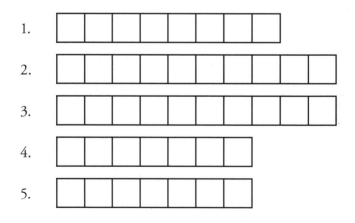

Answers on page 127

# 28

# Southern Food

1. Small pieces of fried pork rind served as a snack.
2. A cut of meat used in a popular soup of the same name. The meat is generally beef or veal, though the name implies otherwise.
3. Classic dish of corn and lima beans.
4. Highly seasoned golden ball of cornmeal fried and served as a side dish.
5. A cornmeal porridge.

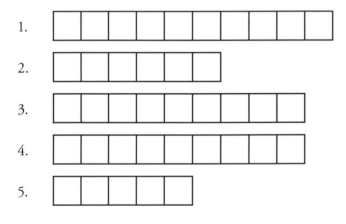

Answers on page 127

# 29

# Taste of Mexico II

1. Salty oval-shaped bread, similar to a baguette. Outer crust is crunchy with a soft inside. Otherwise known as pan de agua, which translates into water bread.
2. Spanish for meat. The "asada" version is a delicious roasted dish. Main ingredient in many Mexican favorites such as tacos or burritos.
3. A green herb with aromatic leaves, often used in Mexican cooking. Also known as Chinese parsley. Its seeds are called coriander.
4. Spanish word for the corn meal used to make corn tortillas. Dried corn is cooked in lime water and cooled, then ground.
5. Mexican word for cheese. Frequently melted and served with chips.

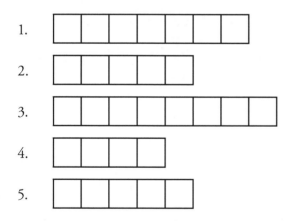

Answers on page 127

# 30

# Tofu

1. Tofu is made by coagulating what ingredient and pressing it into blocks?
2. Firmness is determined by the extraction of what substance?
3. High in what essential compound?
4. First used in what Asian country around 200 B.C.?
5. Variety with creamy, custard-like texture; works well in pureed or blended dishes.

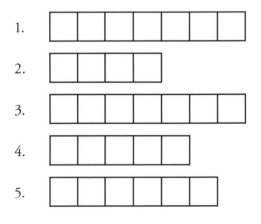

Answers on page 128

# 31

# Taste of Russia

1. Small yeast-leavened buckwheat pancakes traditionally served with sour cream, caviar, or smoked salmon.
2. This soup is frequently served during Russian meals, it can be eaten either hot or cold. Beets are the main ingredient.
3. Fermented beverage often made with black or rye bread. Low alcohol content.
4. Popular dish made with beef and sour cream-based sauce. Invented by a chef who was employed as a Russian general.
5. Porridge dish eaten in Eastern Europe, can be made with any grain as the base ingredient. Either sweet or savory. Traditionally one of the most common foods in Russia.

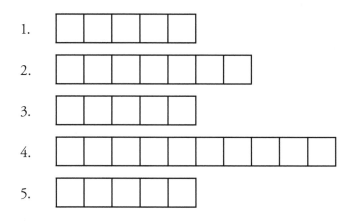

Answers on page 128

# 32

# Beans

1. Small oval-shaped beans with pink or red markings that disappear with cooking. Known for a creamy texture. Flavor similar to chestnuts.
2. Broad beans with long, flattened pods that can measure up to 9 inches. Must be shelled, then cooked and peeled. Sold fresh or dried.
3. Oval in shape, color ranges from white to pink to dark red. Slightly mealy texture. Popular addition to soups, stews, and chili. Available dried or in cans.
4. Small and pea shaped. Green in color when fresh, and tan to black when dried. Versatile ingredient, high in protein and low in carbohydrates. Common in Asian cooking.
5. Mild flavor; round, flat shape. Often referred to as butter beans. Commonly used in soups. Originated in Peru.

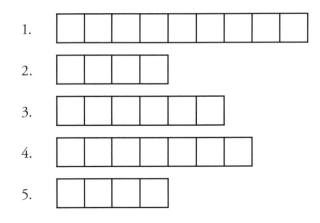

1. ☐☐☐☐☐☐☐☐☐☐
2. ☐☐☐☐
3. ☐☐☐☐☐☐
4. ☐☐☐☐☐☐☐
5. ☐☐☐☐

Answers on page 128

# 33

# Egg Dishes

1. A baked egg dish made with spinach and white sauce.
2. Italian in origin. A variety of fillings can be mixed into the eggs, which are served open faced. Cooking begins on the stovetop, then the pan is placed in the oven and either baked or broiled to finish.
3. Prepared by placing eggs in buttered ramekin dishes and broiling them until the white is set. The yolk remains liquid. Cheese, cream, or herbs are common additions.
4. French dish made from a sauce created with egg yolks and beaten egg whites. Literally means to "puff up".
5. A classic Mexican breakfast dish. Made with fried eggs that are served on top of hot, corn tortillas along with a variety of toppings that often include cheese, black or refried beans, salsa, and avocado.

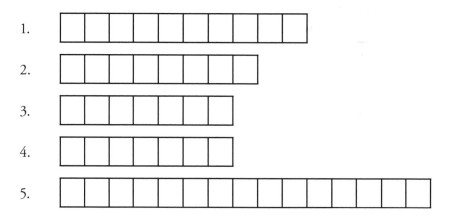

1. ⬜⬜⬜⬜⬜⬜⬜⬜⬜⬜⬜
2. ⬜⬜⬜⬜⬜⬜⬜⬜
3. ⬜⬜⬜⬜⬜⬜⬜
4. ⬜⬜⬜⬜⬜⬜
5. ⬜⬜⬜⬜⬜⬜⬜⬜⬜⬜⬜⬜⬜⬜⬜

Answers on page 128

# 34

# Coffee 101

1. Dorothy Jones, first U.S. coffee trader granted a license to sell coffee in 1670, was from what city?
2. Tannish brown foam that forms on the top of a freshly brewed cup of espresso.
3. Supremo refers to the size of what?
4. Approximately 4,000 to 5,000 coffee beans are required to produce how many Kilograms of roasted coffee?
5. Myth: More of this burns off the longer coffee is roasted.

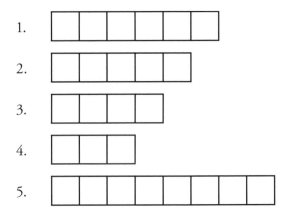

1. ☐☐☐☐☐☐
2. ☐☐☐☐☐
3. ☐☐☐☐
4. ☐☐☐
5. ☐☐☐☐☐☐☐☐

Answers on page 128

# 35

# Thickeners

1. Widely used throughout the food industry as a gelling agent. Found naturally in fruits and vegetables. Often used in jam and jelly recipes.
2. Made with equal amounts of flour and fat. Basic thickening agent for many sauces. Made by melting fat, then whisking in flour and hot liquid.
3. White powder extracted from the root of a West Indian plant. Similar in appearance and texture to cornstarch. Used as a thickening agent for sauces, pie fillings and glazes.
4. A form of dried seaweed traditionally used in Asia and can be substituted for gelatin.
5. A commonly used liquid thickener for pan and wine sauces. Adds a smooth, velvety texture and a rich delicious flavor.

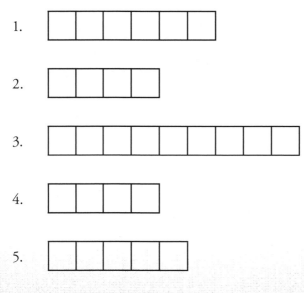

1. ☐☐☐☐☐☐

2. ☐☐☐☐

3. ☐☐☐☐☐☐☐☐☐

4. ☐☐☐

5. ☐☐☐☐☐

Answers on page 128

# 36

# Tabasco

1. What popular drink, invented by an American bartender working in Paris in 1921, consists of tomato juice and Tabasco?
2. Tabasco sauce is made from peppers, salt and what else?
3. Salt for Tabasco is harvested on what island?
4. What family produces the sauce?
5. What university produced a play called "Burlesque Opera of Tabasco" in 1893?

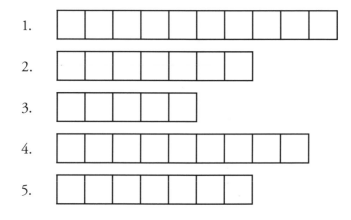

Answers on page 128

# 37

# Chipotle Peppers

1. A chipotle pepper is a smoked and dried version of what other pepper?
2. What cuisine is the chipotle pepper most often used in?
3. Most of these chilies are produced in what Mexican state?
4. These peppers are often ground and blended with other spices to create what sauce?
5. What scale is used to judge the heat value of a pepper?

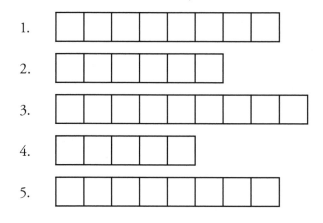

1.
2.
3.
4.
5.

Answers on page 128

# 38

# Horseradish

1. What part of this perennial plant is most often used?
2. The prepared variety is made from grated horseradish and what well known liquid?
3. Horseradish is a member of the Brassicaceae plant family which also includes this ingredient used in a popular yellow condiment?
4. Commercial cultivation of horseradish began in what country in the mid-1800s?
5. Always serve horseradish in a glass or ceramic bowl as it causes silver to do what?

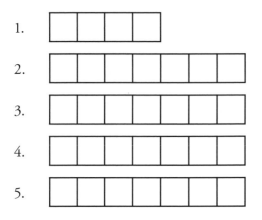

1. ☐☐☐☐
2. ☐☐☐☐☐☐☐
3. ☐☐☐☐☐☐☐
4. ☐☐☐☐☐☐☐
5. ☐☐☐☐☐☐☐

Answers on page 128

# 39

# Potatoes

1. Easily identified by its reddish-brown skin. Most widely used potato in the United States. Good choice for baking, mashing, roasting and frying.
2. White-skinned variety, oblong in shape. Frequently used to make French fries. Also good for boiling, steaming, or roasting.
3. Red potato, smooth, oblong, and slightly flat. Ranges from 1 to 2 inches in diameter. Often used in recipes that call for unpeeled potatoes.
4. Yellow in color, 2 to 4 inches in length, shape is long and slender. This potato is firm and flavorful.
5. Specialty potato with thin, deep purple flesh. Color lightens slightly with cooking.

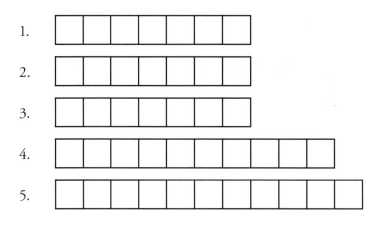

Answers on page 128

# 40

# Gingerbread

1. The first gingerbreads were thought to have originated in which one of the world's seven continents.
2. What is the German word for gingerbread?
3. The quality of the gingerbread in Nuremburg, Germany was so high it was sometimes used as currency to pay what city fee?
4. American bakers of gingerbread often add what sticky, dark colored ingredient?
5. The gingerbread house became popular in Germany after the Hansel and Gretel fairytale was published in the 19th century. What was the last name of the brothers who wrote it?

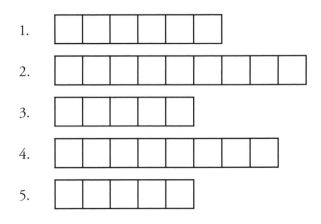

Answers on page 128

# 41

# Potato Chips

1. What century was the potato chip invented?
2. Name for potato chips in Britain.
3. First successfully marketed national brand of potato chips.
4. The potato chip was created after a customer at a New York restaurant sent back this menu item, complaining that it was too thick and soggy. The thin, crispy chip was the replacement.
5. What mechanical machine helped take potato chips from a small specialty item to a top selling snack food?

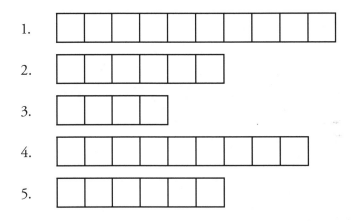

Answers on page 128

# 42

# Sweet Potatoes

1. What town in Kentucky celebrates the sweet potato annually during the month of April?
2. This southern U.S. state is a major producer of sweet potatoes.
3. An orange-colored tuber that is often mistakenly referred to as a sweet potato.
4. In Korean cuisine, the starch from sweet potatoes is used in the production of what type of noodle?
5. Sweet potatoes are high in what essential vitamin?

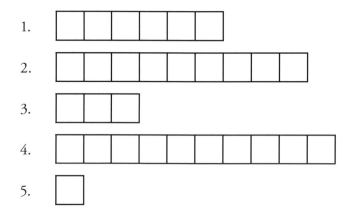

1. ☐☐☐☐☐☐

2. ☐☐☐☐☐☐☐☐☐☐

3. ☐☐☐

4. ☐☐☐☐☐☐☐☐☐☐☐☐

5. ☐

Answers on page 128

# 43

# Tortillas

1. Corn kernels are mixed with what type of citrus-based solution to aid in removal of skins?
2. "Tortilla" came from what Spanish word meaning round cake?
3. A dish made by pressing a very thin layer of masa dough over a mold, then deep frying the dough until crisp, shallow corn cups are formed.
4. After the Spanish brought wheat to the new world, what other popular variety of tortilla was created?
5. A dish made of a small corn tortilla filled and rolled tightly before deep frying.

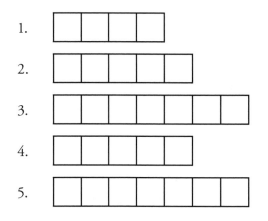

Answers on page 128

# 44

# Salt

1. Variety of additive-free, wider course grained salt. The size of the crystals makes it useful for drawing moisture out of meat.
2. Grey French sea salt hand-harvested with wooden rakes so no metal touches the salt.
3. Salt substance derived from acidic fruits such as lemons or limes. It is dried and forms a powder or crystal with a distinctly sour taste. Also called sour salt.
4. Top-quality salts prized for textures. They dissolve quickly when applied to completed dishes. Includes French sea salt and fleur de sel.
5. Flaky sea salt crystal named for a region in the Atlantic near Essex, England, where it is harvested.

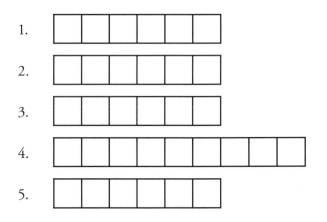

Answers on page 128

# 45

# Abalone

1. Uni-valved, meaning it has one shell and comes from what family?
2. Edible portion is made of what muscle?
3. The flesh is tough; it must be pounded to do what to it prior to cooking?
4. Abalone is known by what other name in Japan?
5. Located along the coastlines of Mexico, California, and Japan, it is found clinging to what solid objects in the water?

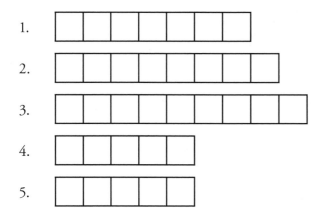

1.

2.

3.

4.

5.

Answers on page 128

# 46

# Garlic

1. Garlic is a member of this family, which also includes leeks and shallots.
2. Most garlic grown domestically comes from this state.
3. Small individual piece of garlic broken off from the bulb to use for cooking.
4. Remove the smell of garlic from your hands by rubbing them with this type of object and water.
5. Hard to believe but true: A psychological term for the intense fear of garlic.

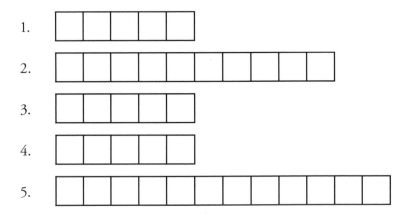

1. ☐☐☐☐☐

2. ☐☐☐☐☐☐☐☐☐☐

3. ☐☐☐☐☐☐

4. ☐☐☐☐☐

5. ☐☐☐☐☐☐☐☐☐☐☐☐☐

Answers on page 128

# 47

# Herring

1. Fillets wrapped in a cylindrical shape around a piece of pickle or onion, then preserved in a spiced vinegar solution.
2. Young herring that are labeled in the United States as salted, smoked, or canned, and packaged in either oil, tomato, or mustard sauce.
3. Marinated in a solution of vinegar and spices prior to being bottled in either a sour cream sauce or a red wine sauce.
4. Split, then cured by salting, drying and cold smoking. Commonly served grilled for breakfast in the United Kingdom and North America.
5. One of the largest types, prized for its eggs. Also known as river herring.

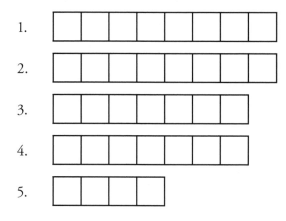

Answers on page 128

# 48

# Tequila

1. This Mexican plant provides the juice that is fermented to make tequila.
2. Addition of this ingredient creates the color variation in tequila.
3. Number of categories of tequila.
4. Worm found in some Mezcal tequila is the larvae of this insect.
5. Popular cocktail that helped boost tequila sales upon its creation in the 1940's.

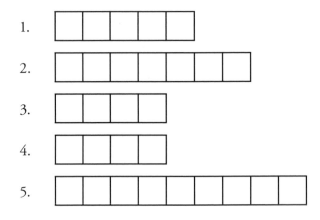

1. ☐☐☐☐☐
2. ☐☐☐☐☐☐☐☐
3. ☐☐☐☐
4. ☐☐☐☐
5. ☐☐☐☐☐☐☐☐☐☐☐

Answers on page 128

# 49

# Soups and Stews

1. Traditional Mediterranean stew prepared with fresh seafood. May include lobster, shrimp, clams, scallops, fish and more. Saffron is an essential ingredient.
2. Prepared with ingredients specific to the region; varieties include New England and Manhattan. Ingredients may include potatoes, meats, seafood, and herbs. Always served hot.
3. Rich, creamy soup that usually consists of puréed seafood or vegetables.
4. Beet base gives it beautiful red color. Often garnished with sour cream. Served hot or cold.
5. Uncooked soup that is always served chilled; contains puréed or chopped fresh vegetables, including tomatoes, onions, peppers, and cucumbers. Originated in southern Spain.

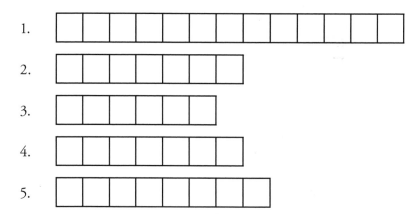

Answers on page 128

# 50

# Flambé

1. Flambé is the French term for what word?
2. Flames from flambé are the result of a chemical reaction between fire and what liquid?
3. One of several popular liquor choices used to flambé.
4. When doing flambé at home, make sure to remove the pan from this before igniting.
5. Fruit used in a popular flambé dish.

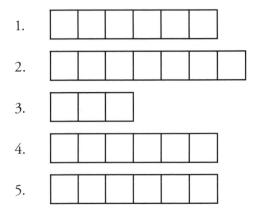

Answers on page 128

# 51

# Asian Sauces

1. Familiar sauce found in the pantry of many home cooks as well as in many Asian restaurants. Naturally fermented from ground soybeans and roasted wheat. Dark colored sauce with generally high salt content, though there are low sodium varieties available.
2. Produced with a combination of ground soybeans, garlic, chiles, and a variety of spices, most commonly five-spice powder. Often used as an ingredient in pork and stir fry dishes.
3. Frequently used as a dipping sauce or marinade. Has a deep, intense color and a sweet flavor.
4. Salty sauce with a thin consistency and pungent flavor. Used in moderation in stir fry dishes.
5. Named after the shell bearing mollusk that is steamed and used to flavor the sauce. Used as a condiment as well as in soups and a variety of Asian dishes.

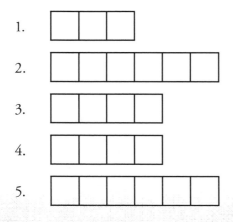

Answers on page 128

# 52

# Taste of Spain

1. Served on tapas menus throughout Spain. Made with fish, ham, chicken, or other fillings encased in breadcrumbs or potatoes and deep fried.
2. Flavorful cold Spanish tomato soup often served as a starter. Ingredients can include cucumbers, peppers, onions, and garlic.
3. The three main ingredient of this popular Valencian dish are rice, saffron and olive oil. The name means "frying pan", which is what the meal is cooked in.
4. An elegant and rich cream-based dessert, a sweet custard topped with caramelized sugar.
5. These fried pastries originated in Spain. They are served hot and are often sprinkled with cinnamon sugar by street vendors.

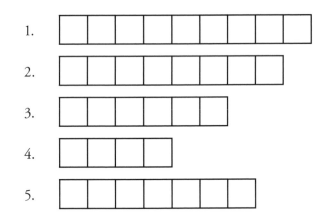

Answers on page 128

# 53

# Taste of Korea

1. This traditional Korean dish is made of salted and fermented vegetables and is eaten at most meals.
2. Traditional meat dish, usually marinated and grilled.
3. A dessert created by combining sticky rice, brown sugar, pine nuts, raisins, red dates, and cinnamon. It is steamed before serving.
4. Best known liquor in Korea; traditionally made from rice.
5. Flavorful, spicy pork sausage filled with a mixture of sweet rice and sweet potato vermicelli noodles. Steamed and cut into round slices. Often sold by street vendors as a delicious snack.

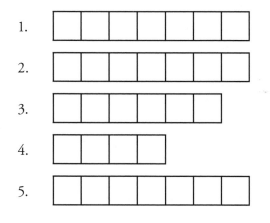

Answers on page 128

# 54

# Taste of Sweden

1. Swedish for "bread and butter table". The well-known name for a buffet boasting a large variety of foods.
2. A popular Scandinavian specialty made with unsalted, dried cod.
3. Swedish spiced punch containing aquavit or brandy.
4. Small, pretzel shaped cookie topped with pearl sugar.
5. Swedish pea soup recipe, traditionally eaten on Thursday's and served with pork and mustard.

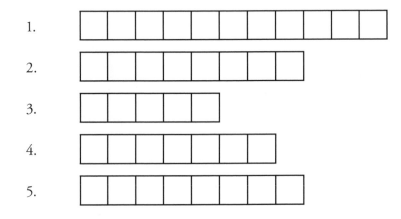

Answers on page 128

# 55

# Cheese

1. A semi-hard, unpasteurized goat's milk cheese from France. Distinct flavor comes from the addition of pepper, parsley, tarragon, and cloves. The color of the rind is deep red.
2. French cheese produced in Corsica. Made from sheep's milk. The small, round wheel has an edible outer rind. The inside is creamy and bright white. The flavor is rich and nutty.
3. Goat's milk cheese native to the Murcia region of Spain. Log shaped with a white outer layer and a creamy, smooth white interior. Taste is mild. Pairs well with breads or seasoned meats.
4. An Italian cheese produced from two separate cow's milking's. Pale yellow with bold, fruity flavor.
5. Pasteurized cow's milk cheese produced in North America. Rind is yellowish orange. The flavor is mild and light. Can be frozen for long periods.

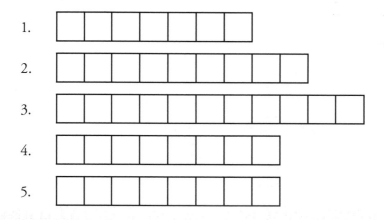

Answers on page 128

# 56

# Tomatoes

1. Small and oval or egg-shaped. Low interior moisture with fewer seeds and a higher solid content than most other tomatoes. Also referred to as a Roma tomato.
2. One of the largest varieties of cultivated tomatoes; big, thick, and meaty. Weighs up to one pound or more. Large enough to be stuffed and baked.
3. Covers a broad range of tomatoes. Name comes from the aging of the seeds or the tradition of nurturing, selecting, and handing down seeds to others for generations.
4. Small and bite size. Bright red in color. Flavor is sweeter than other tomato varieties.
5. Tiniest variety of tomato. Each one weighs approximately 1/8 of an ounce. Either yellow or red. Flesh is intensely flavored, sweet, and crisp.

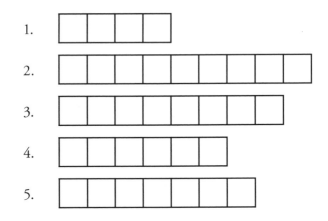

Answers on page 128

# 57

# Christmas Pudding Treasures

1. Discovery of this small silver token in pudding is said to bring wealth to its recipient.
2. Symbolizes good luck in the coming year.
3. Signifies spinsterhood. Hint: covers thumb while sewing.
4. Symbolizes safe travels throughout the upcoming year. Hint: necessary piece of heavy equipment if you want to moor your boat to the bottom of the lake or ocean.
5. Discovery of this piece of jewelry could indicate impending marriage.

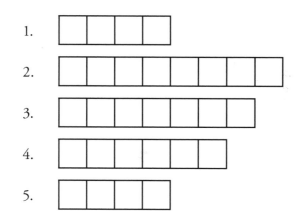

Answers on page 128

# 58

# Organic Gardening

1. Term that means the legal requirements for organic standards have been met.
2. Name of crops planted close to one another for the mutual benefit of growth, they may repel certain insects or pests or attracting beneficial ones. They may also provide wind protection, shade, or nutrient enrichment for one another.
3. Spreading materials such as compost, straw, or wood chips to help conserve moisture for the crops while also stemming the growth of weeds.
4. Abbreviation for the type of farm funded by a community group. Members pay a fee and receive a wide assortment of fresh-picked produce weekly through the growing season.
5. Crops planted separately for the specific purpose of luring pests and insects away from an economic crop which is grown to sell for profit.

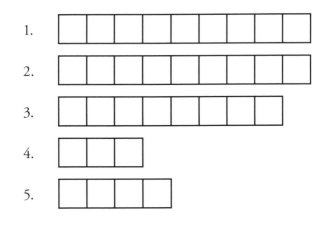

Answers on page 128

# 59

# Cauliflower

1.  While most of a cauliflower is edible, this part is consumed most often.
2.  The name for cauliflower comes from the Latin word "caulis" which means stalk and "floris" which means what?
3.  When planted in an optimal climate, cauliflower can yield how many crops in one year?
4.  The top of the cauliflower is sometimes called this due to its white lumpy appearance.
5.  Cauliflower is part of what plant family?

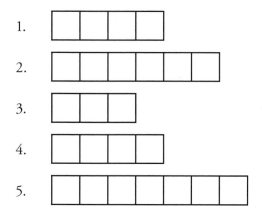

Answers on page 128

# 60

# **Beauty Foods**

1. High in Vitamin B, which aids in skin cell restoration and hair growth. A few unsalted versions contain protein, fiber, and monounsaturated fats.
2. The green flesh of this food is high in healthy fats and can be used as a face mask.
3. Great source of Omega-3 fatty acids. Enhances the body's ability to improve circulation and helps keep the outer layers of skin smooth. Reduces inflammation.
4. Deeply colored blue fruit, high in antioxidants.
5. A bivalve mollusk rich in zinc, low in calories, high in copper and iron.

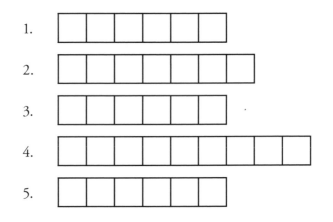

Answers on page 128

# 61

# Asian Soups

1. Popular soup with two defining flavors made from red peppers and vinegar. Usually meat-based; key ingredients include bamboo shoots, tofu, and wood ear fungus.
2. Japanese stock used as a base for a variety of soups, dipping sauces, and main dishes. Common ingredients include dried kelp, dried bonito flakes and dried shiitake mushrooms.
3. This soup includes chicken broth, green onions, and the main ingredient, which is dropped in after being beaten, hence the name.
4. Transparent noodle made of starch and water. Becomes clear when boiled. Also known as bean threads or Chinese vermicelli, it is often called for in Asian soup recipes.
5. This is a Vietnamese soup made of beef or chicken stock. Ingredients can include rice noodles, thinly sliced pieces of beef or chicken, and a variety of flavorful herbs and spices.

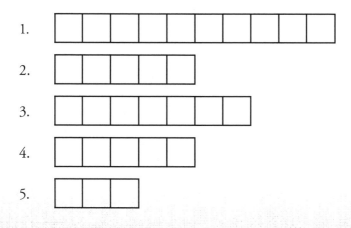

Answers on page 128

# 62

# Avocados

1. Most common and well-known avocado in the United States. Purplish-black skin has a pebble like texture. Skin continues to darken as it ripens.
2. Large and round, also known as the summertime variety. Skin is thick and dark green. Flesh is buttery yellow.
3. Long pear-like shape. Flesh is pale green and contains a small seed.
4. Avocados are part of what food group?
5. Avocado flesh begins to discolor when exposed to air. Application of what type of fruit juice helps to prevent this.

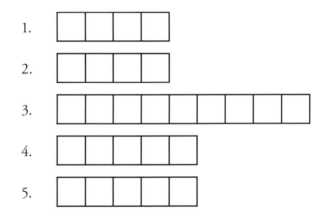

1. ☐☐☐☐
2. ☐☐☐☐
3. ☐☐☐☐☐☐☐☐☐
4. ☐☐☐☐☐
5. ☐☐☐☐☐

Answers on page 128

# 63

# Artichokes

1. California city currently known as the artichoke capital of the world.
2. In which U.S. state were artichokes first grown after being brought in by settlers around the 19<sup>th</sup> century?
3. What is the last name of the famous blonde actress who was crowned the first queen of artichokes in 1974? Think Norma Jean.
4. Artichoke flavored aperitif produced in Italy.
5. Leaf-like pieces that make up the bud of the artichoke.

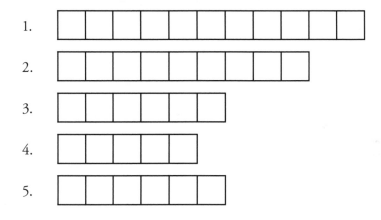

Answers on page 128

# 64

# Pasta

1. Small, rice shaped pasta, often used in soups or salads.
2. Flat, long noodle with fluted edges. Used in a popular layered Italian dish.
3. Small crescent or moon shaped tube pasta. Type of macaroni.
4. Means "butterfly" in Italian. Shaped into rectangular or oval patterns that are pinched in the middle. Also called bowtie pasta.
5. Refers to desired texture of cooked pasta. Literally means "to the tooth"

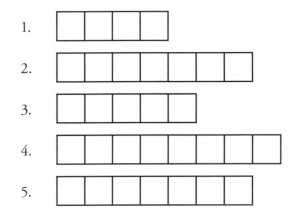

Answers on page 128

# 65

# Maple Syrup

1. Name for the procedure used to remove sap from a maple tree.
2. A mature maple tree produces about how many gallons of sap in a season?
3. Maple trees are not tapped for syrup until they are at least how many years old to avoid damage to the tree.
4. Maple syrup is graded according to density and what additional characteristic?
5. Tree's store this in their stems and roots prior to the winter season; It is then converted to sugar and rises in the sap in the spring.

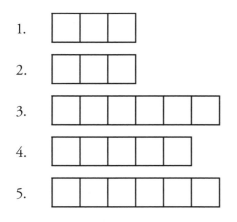

Answers on page 128

# 66

# Truffles

1. Dogs, pigs, and goats, use what sense to help them locate truffles underground?
2. Truffles are classified as part of what kingdom? Hint: this kingdom does not require photosynthesis but rather obtains its nutrients by absorbing them from their surroundings. Mushrooms also fall into this category.
3. The best-known truffles are what color?
4. Many truffles are found in the forests of Périgord located in what European country?
5. During the truffle growing process it is extremely important to establish a relationship between the tuber melanosporum and the host tree. What tree requires minimal pruning and has the ability to sustain truffle production over a long period of time?

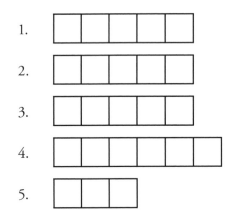

1. ☐☐☐☐☐

2. ☐☐☐☐☐

3. ☐☐☐☐☐

4. ☐☐☐☐☐☐

5. ☐☐☐

Answers on page 128

# 67

# Taste of Italy

1. Name for a sauce, stew, or hearty pasta sauce, often containing meat, tomatoes, onions, vegetables, and a variety of seasonings.
2. General name for all cured pork products.
3. Bitter Italian aperitif usually mixed with soda water.
4. Italian name for a tomato.
5. Elongated white bean is also known as a white kidney bean; often used in Italian cooking.

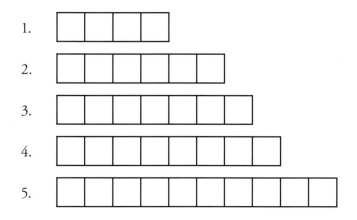

Answers on page 128

# 68

# High Altitude Cooking

1. At high altitudes, this process occurs at lower temperatures.
2. Does microwave cooking take more or less time at higher altitudes?
3. High altitude areas are prone to lower humidity, which produces an increased moisture loss and causes what process to accelerate?
4. Cooking at higher altitudes generally takes longer. To prevent food from drying out, what should you do with pots and pans?
5. Using this variety of eggs when baking at high altitudes gives added moisture and structure to baked goods.

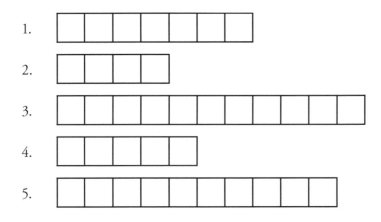

1.
2.
3.
4.
5.

Answers on page 128

# 69

# Bread

1. Polish sweet yeast bread is cake-like in texture. Rum scented and often flavored with raisins, almonds, and grated orange peel.
2. Mexican roll shaped like a football. Outer crust is crispy with a light and chewy interior.
3. Name of this bread is Italian for slipper. Loaf is wide and long with a soft inside and a crisp outer crust.
4. If a bread crust becomes thick, porous, or too brown during the baking process, too much of this ingredient was used.
5. What ingredient prevents bread dough from sticking to surfaces during the kneading process?

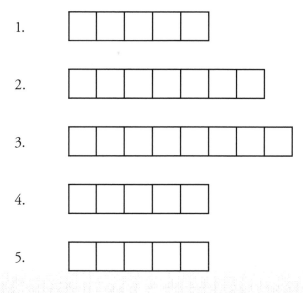

1. ⬚⬚⬚⬚⬚

2. ⬚⬚⬚⬚⬚⬚

3. ⬚⬚⬚⬚⬚⬚⬚

4. ⬚⬚⬚⬚

5. ⬚⬚⬚⬚⬚

Answers on page 129

# 70

# Waffles

1. A culinary specialty in what European country?
2. The word waffle comes from what Dutch word?
3. In 1953, three brothers introduced this frozen toaster version.
4. Belgian waffles are made with yeast, while most American recipes contain what leavening agent?
5. Popular appliance first patented by Cornelius Swarthout of New York in 1869.

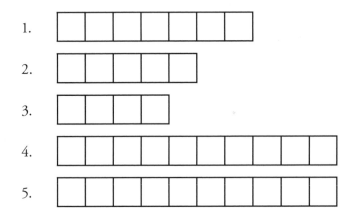

Answers on page 129

# 71

# Chocolate

1. The name given to a class of high-quality chocolate, often used for dipping truffles or candies.
2. Dark chocolate with a small proportion of sugar. Has deeper chocolate flavor than semisweet.
3. Contains powdered or condensed milk and has about 20 percent cocoa solids. Most popular eating chocolate. Found in many candy bars.
4. Visual result of cocoa butter crystals rising to the surface and causing gray discoloration. Does not affect flavor. Occurs when chocolate is old or not stored properly.
5. Process by which chocolate is stabilized through a method of melting and cooling. Often done when making candy or coating truffles.

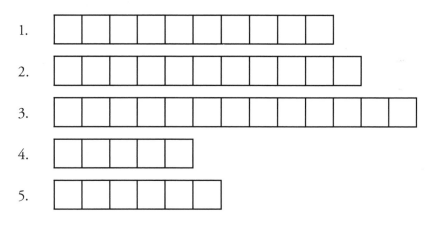

Answers on page 129

# 72

# Top Chef Trivia

1. Cooking challenge on Bravo's Top Chef TV show where each chef is given specific ingredients or a certain theme to follow with very little time to complete the dish. The guest chef chooses the winner and he or she is usually exempt from the following elimination challenge.
2. The winner of Top Chef gets a spread in this culinary magazine, along with $250,000 to start their own restaurant.
3. Lead judge on Top Chef. He is a former executive chef of Gramercy Tavern in New York City, and has received five James Beard awards for his cooking achievements.
4. First name of the host of Top Chef since season two. She is an Indian American cookbook author, as well as a model and actress.
5. At the end of each episode, following the elimination challenge, one of the contestants is instructed to "please pack your……and go".

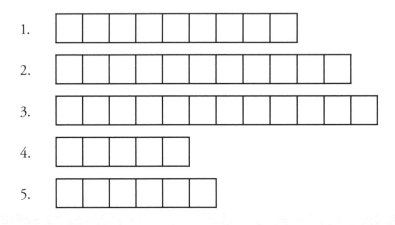

Answers on page 129

# 73

# Taste of Ireland

1. Traditional potato pancake produced with finely grated raw potato, mashed potatoes with flour, baking soda, buttermilk and occasionally egg. Made as griddle bread or dumplings.
2. Classic recipe is a stove-top casserole that includes sausage, ham, potato, and onion. This is a hearty meal. It is especially popular in Dublin.
3. Yeasted raisin bread most often purchased in flat rounds. The dough is sweeter than sandwich bread.
4. Popular beer that originated in the St. James' Gate Brewery in Dublin almost 250 years ago.
5. A cocktail made with a caffeinated beverage, combined with whiskey and sugar (and sometimes Irish cream). This drink is topped with dollops of whipped cream and served warm.

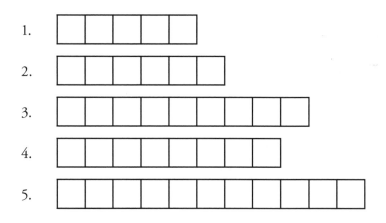

1. ☐☐☐☐☐
2. ☐☐☐☐☐☐
3. ☐☐☐☐☐☐☐☐☐
4. ☐☐☐☐☐☐☐☐
5. ☐☐☐☐☐☐☐☐☐☐☐☐

Answers on page 129

# 74

# Cooking Techniques

1. To plunge food, usually produce, into boiling water briefly, then quickly remove and immerse it in ice water in order to halt the cooking process and retain color.
2. To render solid foods into a mashed, smooth substance.
3. To boil down a liquid with the purpose of intensifying flavor.
4. To spoon or ladle sauce over heated food; often done with eggs or meat.
5. To remove accumulated fat from the surface of hot liquid.

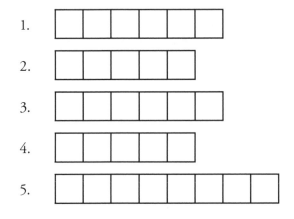

1. ☐☐☐☐☐☐☐
2. ☐☐☐☐☐
3. ☐☐☐☐☐☐
4. ☐☐☐☐☐
5. ☐☐☐☐☐☐☐☐☐

Answers on page 129

# 75

# Pastry Tools

1. Used to cut cold fat, butter or shortening, into a dry flour mixture to allow even distribution of the fat without warming it up. This tool consists of a parallel set of curved wires attached to a handle.
2. Bristles attached to a wooden or plastic handle. Comes in different sizes and widths.
3. This is a thin piece of flexible plastic that is used to clean up scraps of dough from the inside of bowls or rolling surfaces.
4. Made of pieces of mesh or cloth that fit over a rolling pin. Used to roll out doughs that are delicate and can tear easily.
5. Filled and used to shape batters and doughs. When fitted with a tip, it can be used to decorate pastries, cakes, and cookies.

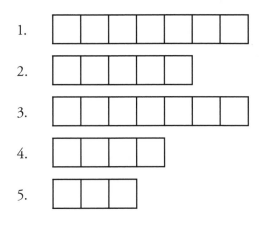

1. ⬜⬜⬜⬜⬜⬜⬜
2. ⬜⬜⬜⬜⬜
3. ⬜⬜⬜⬜⬜⬜⬜
4. ⬜⬜⬜
5. ⬜⬜

Answers on page 129

# 76

# Champagne

1. Dry variety of champagne with crisp and fruity flavors. Contains little or no residual sugar in the final product so it is not overly sweet.
2. A blend of several non-sparkling wines. The prestige versions are considered some of the finest champagnes produced. Dom Perignon fits into this category.
3. Has a slightly pink tint because of the addition of a little red wine or contact with the skin of red grapes.
4. Sweet champagne that has between 3.3 and 5 percent residual sugar. Rich flavor makes it a great choice to serve with desserts or with blue veined cheeses.
5. Champagne is the name of a region in the northern part of this vast wine producing country.

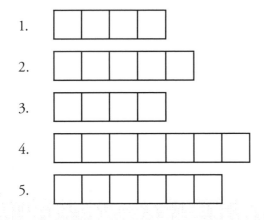

Answers on page 129

# 77

# Steak Dishes

1. Classic French dish that is patted dry, then coated and rubbed with ground white, black or green peppercorns. New York strip or sirloin is often used for the best flavor.
2. Restaurant preparation is done tableside with cognac or brandy and a burst of flames. Served with a rich cream sauce that may include shallots, thyme, Dijon mustard, and mushrooms.
3. Served raw and made by finely slicing a high grade of meat such as New York strip or filet mignon. Can be marinated in red wine and served with herbs and seasonings or onions. Occasionally, a raw egg is added.
4. Beef that is rolled and pounded, then dredged in seasoned flour and slow-cooked. The pounding tenderizes the meat. Usually made with a tougher cut of meat such as a round steak.
5. Ground beef mixed with eggs, milk, and various seasonings then shaped into patties that resemble a steak. Can be baked, broiled, or fried.

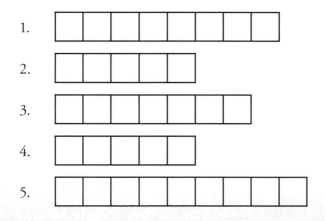

Answers on page 129

# Cookies of the Globe

1. Native to Austria; usually made of ground almonds. Once baked, warm jam is spread on the top of a cookie, which is then topped by another cookie that has had the center cut out to form a "window".
2. Traditional Italian cookie with anise flavor. It is made with a special iron and resembles a waffle.
3. These spicy Scandinavian cookies are fried in oil using a hand-held iron, then dusted with powdered sugar. The name alludes to a popular flower.
4. Dutch cookies traditionally baked on December 5th, the eve of the feast of St. Nicholas.
5. Delicate French cookies baked, then draped carefully over a rolling pin to form a lovely shape as they cool. The name of this cookie is French for tile.

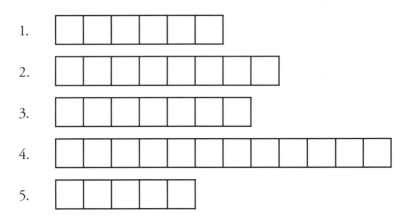

Answers on page 129

# 79

# Cracker Jacks

1.  This snack is a combination of popcorn, peanuts, and what dark syrupy ingredient?
2.  The catch phrase "A ….. in every box was coined in 1912 when toys were inserted in every package.
3.  What well-known company purchased the Cracker Jack brand from Borden in 1997?
4.  What is the full name of the trademark character on the front of the Cracker Jack box? Hint: he appears with his dog bingo.
5.  The popular song written by Jack Norwroth, sung during a break during baseball games, has the lyrics "Take me out to the ball game" and "buy me some peanuts and Cracker Jacks". At what inning is this sung?

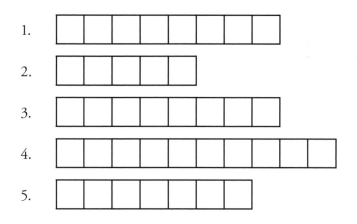

Answers on page 129

# 80

# Chef's Tools

1. Used for lifting food out of hot oil. It serves as both a spoon and strainer.
2. Tool that has become an important kitchen accessory often used to grate, either finely, for zesting, or more coarsely, for chocolate or cheese.
3. Very sharp, multi-purpose tool used to slice vegetables into varying shapes and thickness.
4. Mesh screen often used to break up lumps and aerate flour before baking. The result is that it takes up more volume than it did prior to using this tool.
5. Specific type of kitchen knife with a characteristic saw-like blade.

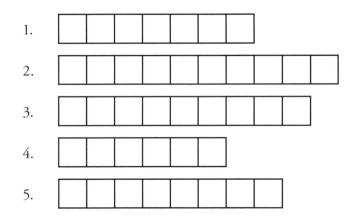

1. □□□□□□□
2. □□□□□□□□□□□
3. □□□□□□□□□□
4. □□□□□□
5. □□□□□□□□

Answers on page 129

# 81

# Grill Types

1. Traditional-style Japanese grill has a small metal firebox with grates that are positioned over the coals.
2. Bowl-shaped grill in which coals are placed in the center with the grill grates positioned directly above the coals. Temperature can be controlled by opening and closing the vents.
3. Functions like an inverted broiler. Food lacks the flavor that is obtained with a conventional grill.
4. Some of these can be used to grill food or impart even more flavor in the meat/protein by slow cooking for several hours. Wood chips are often used in this process. Hickory is one of the most popular wood chip flavors for this process.
5. Convenient, starts at the touch of a button. Offers consistent and controllable temperatures.

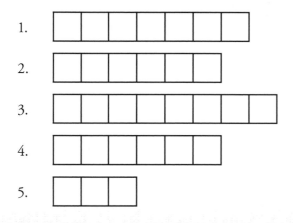

Answers on page 129

# 82

# Candy Corn

1. Made of a combination of sugar, corn syrup and what other ingredient?
2. It is intended to look like what food item?
3. Is white at the tip, orange in the center and what color at the widest end?
4. Approximately how many calories does 11 pieces of candy corn contain?
5. Which company is currently the top branded producer of candy corn?

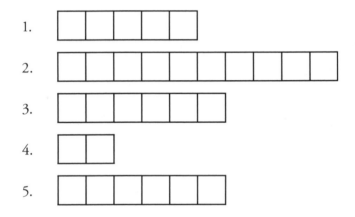

Answers on page 129

# 83

# Sweet Treats

1. Thick sauce made of puréed fruits or vegetables.
2. Formal name for distillates or extracts used to flavor sweet or savory dishes.
3. An Eggless custard served well-chilled. Italian name means "cooked cream".
4. Layers of puff pastry with a cream filling.
5. Semi-frozen mixture similar in taste and consistency to sorbet and Italian ice.

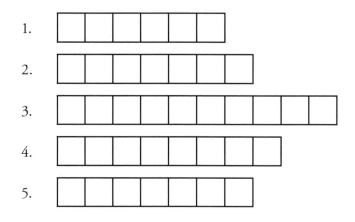

1. ☐☐☐☐☐☐
2. ☐☐☐☐☐☐☐
3. ☐☐☐☐☐☐☐☐☐☐
4. ☐☐☐☐☐☐☐☐
5. ☐☐☐☐☐☐☐☐

Answers on page 129

# 84

# Cookware

1. Thin coating prevents sticking and has a fairly high heat resistance. Frequently used to coat frying pans.
2. Heavy pan that distributes heat evenly and retains heat well.
3. Light and affordable, this material resists rust and is an effective heat conductor.
4. Excellent thermal conductivity. Pans are prone to tarnish with exposure to air. Using a bowl with this type of material is highly recommended for whipping egg whites.
5. Considered one of the best surfaces for cookware. Most of this type of cookware is anodized, which prevents unsafe materials from leaking into the food.

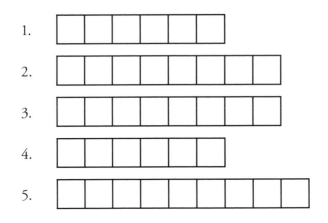

Answers on page 129

# 85

# Taste of New Orleans

1. Similar in size and shape to a submarine sandwich. Ingredients often include seafood; usually served hot.
2. Pastry formed into 3-inch square and fried, then sprinkled with powdered sugar. Popular item on the menu at Café Du Monde.
3. Well-known Creole dish that can be made with a variety of ingredients, the main ones being rice, meat, vegetables, and spices.
4. Spicy stew, with rice that is cooked separately, and added before serving.
5. This Sandwich starts with Sicilian bread and is layered with a traditional olive salad and multiple layers of meat and cheese.

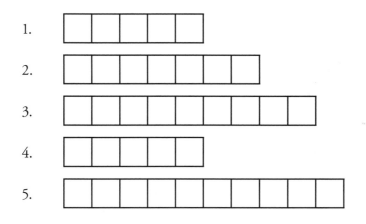

1. ☐☐☐☐☐
2. ☐☐☐☐☐☐
3. ☐☐☐☐☐☐☐☐
4. ☐☐☐☐
5. ☐☐☐☐☐☐☐☐☐

Answers on page 129

# 86

# Honey

1. Sweet substance secreted by flowers; this is necessary to create honey.
2. A honeycomb cell contains how many sides?
3. Worker bees secrete this substance from glands in their abdomen; it is used to form the cups and walls of the honeycomb.
4. The more of this substance honey contains, the more likely it is to crystalize and become thick or "set".
5. Name for a beekeeper.

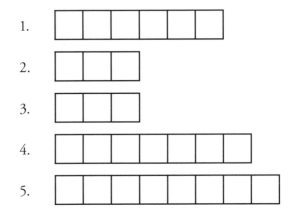

Answers on page 129

# 87

# Anatomy of a cookie

1. Provides ample richness and moisture to a cookie. Melts during cooking and causes cookies to spread.
2. Provides most of the water in cookies and contains essential proteins. The higher the proportion of this in a recipe, the more cake-like the texture will be.
3. Keeps cookies tender and enhances "puffing" during baking.
4. When creamed or beaten with other ingredients, this introduces air bubbles into mix and lightens cookie texture. Important flavor component in many dessert recipes.
5. Most cookies are made with either all-purpose or pastry version.

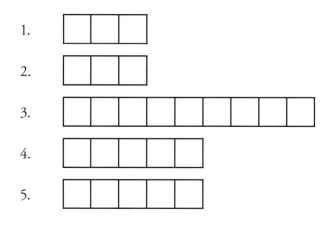

1. ▢▢▢
2. ▢▢▢
3. ▢▢▢▢▢▢▢▢▢
4. ▢▢▢▢▢
5. ▢▢▢▢▢

Answers on page 129

# 88

# Baklava

1. Baklava is a traditional dessert in Turkey and what other Mediterranean country?
2. Type of pastry sheet that forms the base of this dessert.
3. Traditional shape that it is cut into for serving.
4. They are coarsely ground and sprinkled over the top.
5. An ingredient in the syrup that is poured over the top.

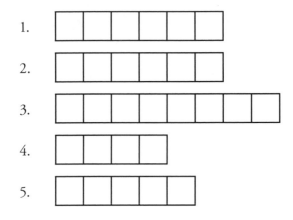

Answers on page 129

# Italian Desserts

1.  This drink is a great alternative to an iced coffee. Consists of a scoop of vanilla or chocolate gelato or ice cream, topped with a shot of hot espresso.
2.  This classic Italian macaroon is light, crunchy, and has the very distinct flavor of almond.
3.  Made by whisking together egg yolks with wine, most often marsala, and sugar. The beating of the yolks takes place over simmering water, so they cook while forming a light and foamy custard that is whipped.
4.  Frozen molded dessert with two layers of ice cream and a rum flavored whipped cream between them.
5.  Fruit filled sweet yeast bread that hails from Milan and is a popular treat in Italy during the Christmas season, baked in a tall cylindrical, straight-sided mold.

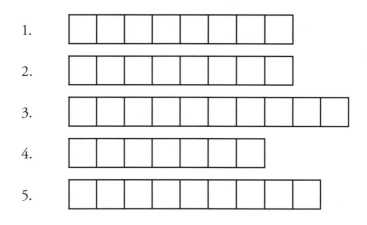

Answers on page 129

# 90

# Salmon

1. Also known as Chinook salmon. Weighs an average of 20 pounds but can reach up to 120 pounds and can grow to be 40 inches long. The distinguishing characteristics include white to bright red flesh and dots on the back and dorsal fins.
2. Highly prized for canning. Flesh is firm and deep red in color. Weight averages 6 to 9 pounds. It accounts for up to 30 percent of Alaska's commercial harvest.
3. Often sold whole in commercial fish markets. Delicious smoked. Recognized by its metallic silver or bluish-black coloration.
4. Smallest of the salmon varieties, with the lightest color and lowest fat content. Their pale flesh makes them less desirable than salmon with pink flesh. Also known as the dog variety due to the hooked snout with sharp, canine-like teeth.
5. Named after one of the longest and most rugged rivers in Alaska. Rich and nutty flavor. Only available for three to four weeks each year.

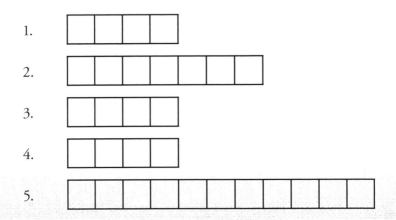

1. ☐☐☐☐

2. ☐☐☐☐☐☐

3. ☐☐☐

4. ☐☐☐

5. ☐☐☐☐☐☐☐☐☐☐☐

Answers on page 129

# 91

# **Wine Bottles**

1. Contains 187 ml or ¼ of a standard bottle.
2. Equivalent of 1.5 liters or 2 standard bottles of wine.
3. The still wine variety contains 4.5 liters or 6 standard bottles.
4. 12 liters or 16 standard bottles.
5. Holds 9 liters or 12 regular bottles.

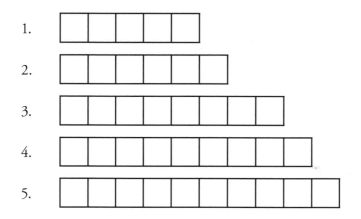

Answers on page 129

# 92

# Game Birds

1. Medium-size bird found in North America and Europe, weighs between 2.5 pounds and 5 pounds. Sometimes farm raised.
2. Small, plump bird that generally walks rather than flies. Makes its nest on the ground and is not migratory. Also called a partridge.
3. Medium to large migratory bird often found near water. Weighs from 5 to 18 pounds. This bird is high in fat.
4. State bird of Alaska. In the winter, both male and female molt to white except for their tail, which remains black.
5. North America's largest game bird. Its head changes color when it becomes excited. The wild variety can run up to 20 miles per hour and fly, for short distances at 55 mph.

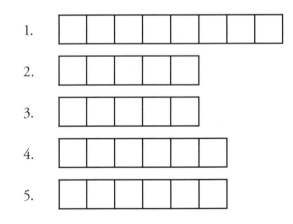

Answers on page 129

# 93

# Julia Child

1. What college did Julia attend?
2. Northeast city where the Child's moved after Paris.
3. Prestigious culinary school that Julia Child attended.
4. French chef who collaborated with her on television programs and cookbooks.
5. The U.S. Navy rejected her because she was too….?

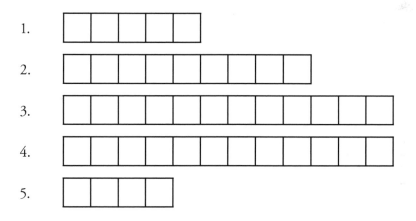

Answers on page 129

# 94

# Meringue

1. Made by combining powdered sugar and what part of the egg?
2. Uses a binding agent of cornstarch or cream of what?
3. This weather element is one of the most critical factors in making a successful meringue.
4. Is beaten until what forms?
5. The smallest bit of what part of the egg will ruin a meringue.

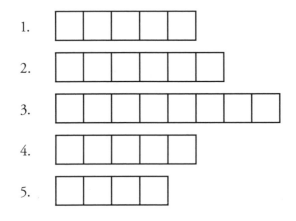

Answers on page 129

# 95

# State Fair Foods

1. Popular batter-dipped frankfurter on a stick.
2. Fried cake sprinkled with powdered sugar.
3. Deep-fried dairy product.
4. This "blooming" treat is dipped in batter and deep-fried.
5. Round confections served warm and sprinkled with sugar.

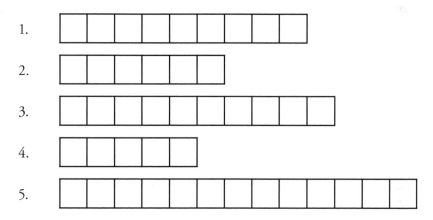

Answers on page 129

# 96

# Wraps

1. Leaves used in Southeast Asia to wrap and tie packets of rice, fish, or vegetables before steaming.
2. Large leaves found in the tropics and used to wrap meat or rice or to line the bottoms of barbecue pits. They add a subtle hint of anise fragrance and flavor to food cooked inside.
3. Leaves often used in Greek or Middle Eastern cooking. Difficult to find fresh. Purchased bottled or canned and soaked in a brine. They need to be thoroughly rinsed and blanched before use.
4. Type of wrap used in Japanese cooking to make stuffed dumplings. They stretch and seal well, and do not tear easily. Once filled they ban be steamed, boiled, or fried.
5. Thin wrappers are used to make this savory Filipino egg roll. Made from either flour and water or cornstarch, eggs, and water. Once filled, they are fried and served as an appetizer or a side dish.

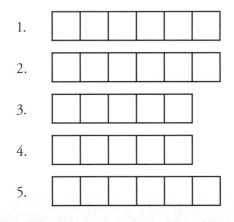

Answers on page 129

# 97

# **Bourbon**

1. Bourbon is what type of American liquor?
2. What are new, charred oak barrels used for?
3. Bourbon is made of more than two-thirds of what cereal grain?
4. Kentucky city known as the bourbon capital of the world.
5. Popular bourbon-based drink.

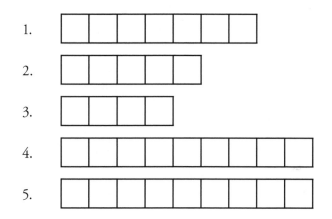

Answers on page 129

# 98

# Beer

1. Established in 1844 in Milwaukee. First beer to win a blue ribbon at the Chicago World's Fair in 1893. Also famously known as "PBR". The "P" stands for what?
2. Brewery that opened in 1852 in St. Louis and is the largest in the United States. A zoological park in Tampa Bay, Fla. bears part of the company name.
3. Pioneer in Canadian brewing since 1786 when it was founded on the banks of the St. Lawrence river in Montreal. Bears the founder's last name.
4. Name prior to its purchase in 1863 was the De Hooiberg brewery, and it was the largest in Amsterdam. First brewery to export to the United States after prohibition ended.
5. First export shipment from Dublin, Ireland, to England had about 6 barrels of this beer in 1769. One of the main ingredients in the popular "black and tan."

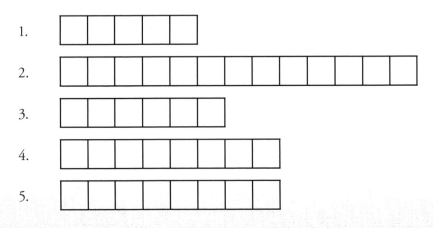

Answers on page 129

# 99

# Sourdough

1. Middle Eastern country known as one of the first to create sourdough bread.
2. When dough is kneaded, this protein helps retain the leavening's gas bubbles that create a light structure in the bread.
3. A foamy wild-yeast mixture used as the base and leavening agent for some breads.
4. U.S. city known for its superior sourdough bread.
5. Another name for the round shape this bread is historically baked into.

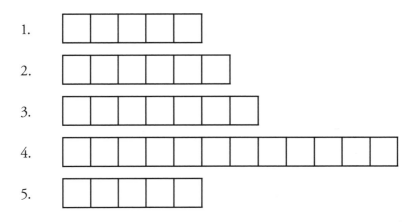

Answers on page 129

# 100

# Sauces

1. Popular Italian sauce made with a combination of heavy cream, butter, garlic, and fresh grated parmesan cheese. Created in the 1920's by a Roman restaurateur.
2. Argentinian herb sauce made with olive oil, lemon or vinegar, parsley, dried oregano, and garlic. Often used as meat topping, marinade, or as a dipping sauce for empanadas.
3. Mixture of either ketchup or chili sauce combined with horseradish, lemon juice and hot sauce. Often served with oysters or shrimp.
4. Spanish combination of almonds or hazelnuts, olive oil, roasted garlic, and red pepper. May include red wine vinegar, tomatoes, onions, fennel, or mint. Usually served with roasted vegetables, fish, or poultry.
5. Mixture of butter, cream, egg yolks, sherry, and seasonings used to accompany shellfish.

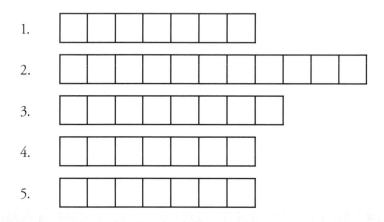

Answers on page 129

# 101

# Oats

1. Also called old fashioned oats, this variety is made by steaming and flattening the oats. The cooking time is about 15 minutes.
2. Oats that have been sliced into many pieces before being steamed and rolled into very thin flakes. They cook in about 5 minutes.
3. Made with cut groats (hulled grains of the oats) that have been pre-cooked and dried prior to being rolled. This type of oatmeal is mixed and packaged with sugar, salt, and other flavorings. It is ready to eat almost immediately after mixing with warm water or milk.
4. Oat product made from groats that are cut into 2 or 3 pieces, then ground into a fine powder. It is the essential ingredient in bread. Mainstay in most home kitchen pantries.
5. Name for the outer casing of the oat. High in soluble fiber, which has been found to help in lowering cholesterol.

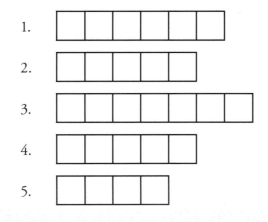

Answers on page 129

# 102

# Almonds

1. It takes approximately 2.5 million of these colonies to pollinate California's 1.2 million acres of almond crops.
2. It takes how many pounds of almonds to make one pint of almond oil?
3. Considered to be one of the finest cultivated almonds. This variety is large, plump, and often sold with a hard, colored, sugar coating.
4. Almonds are known to be what type of fruit? Hint: They are in the same family as cherries, plums, and peaches.
5. The manufacturer of what popular product utilizes 40 percent of the world's almond crop.

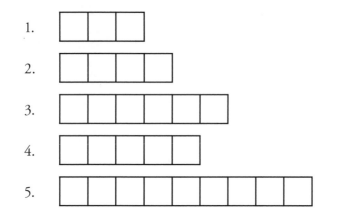

Answers on page 129

# 103

# Vanilla

1. An organic crystal that forms on the outside of the vanilla bean as it dries.
2. A sweetened, highly concentrated form of vanilla extract that still contains the seeds from the bean. Useful in recipes where little addition of liquid is desired.
3. Fine, off-white substance is made of sugar or sucrose laced with the flavor of vanilla. Good for flavoring beverages as it dissolves easily when stirred into liquid.
4. An extract not artificially derived. Contains varied amounts of corn syrup, sugar, caramel colors, and stabilizers as well as at least 35 percent alcohol.
5. Region where about 75 percent of vanilla beans come from, situated off the southeast coast of Africa.

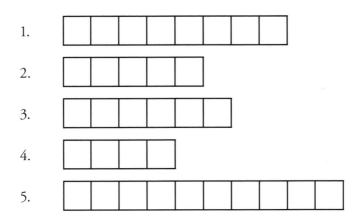

Answers on page 129

# 104

# International Drinks

1. Lemon-flavored liqueur produced in southern Italy. Made from a combination of lemon rinds, sugar, alcohol, and water.
2. Greek iced drink with foam, made with instant coffee.
3. Traditional egg and cream beverage served primarily during the months of November and December in the United States. It is often used in the popular Tom and Jerry cocktail.
4. Indian drink consisting of a blend of yogurt, water, ice, and spices, mixed until frothy.
5. Puerto Rican coconut rum beverage popular during the Christmas season. Made of sweetened condensed milk, dark rum, coconut milk, water, and ground cinnamon.

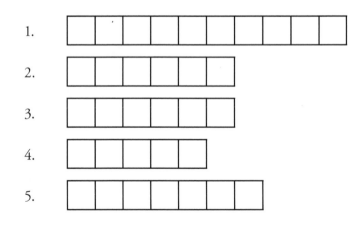

Answers on page 129

# 105

# Irish Whiskey

1. Distilled how many times during the production process?
2. Irish whiskey is aged in what type of cast?
3. Variety of whiskey made with only 1 type of malted grain and distilled at only 1 distillery.
4. Water and barley are mixed with ground barley grist to create what ingredient necessary for whiskey production?
5. Name of Ireland's oldest working whiskey distillery?

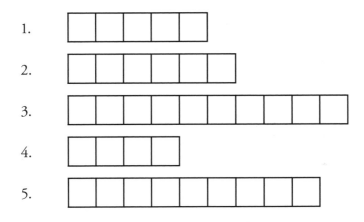

Answers on page 129

# 106

# Candy Canes

1. The first candy canes were straight and were this single color.
2. The first reference to traditionally shaped candy canes comes from this country in about 1670 when the choirmaster of the Cologne Cathedral bent the sticks into canes to represent the Shepard's staff.
3. This is one of the most recognizable candy cane flavors.
4. The color of the vibrant stripe that runs through candy canes today.
5. Throughout history candy canes have been used to decorate this item in homes around the world during the holidays.

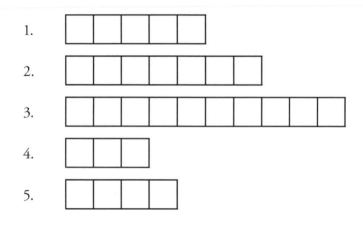

Answers on page 130

# 107

# Vegetarian Options

1. This diet restricts meat consumption to only poultry and fowl. It is considered "semi-vegetarian." Red meat, fish and seafood are excluded.
2. Vegetarian who includes dairy products and eggs in their diet.
3. One who mostly follows a plant-based diet but occasionally eats fish, meat, or dairy. Not technically considered vegetarian.
4. One who eats seafood but not meat, poultry, or fowl. Also considered "semi-vegetarian."
5. This diet excludes red or white meat, fowl, fish, or dairy products. Egg products are allowed.

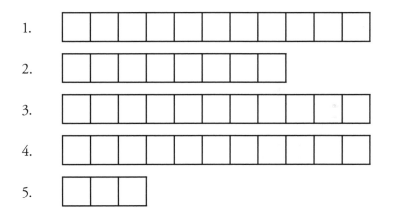

Answers on page 130

# 108

# Flavorful Plants

1. Aromatic member of the grass family that forms clumps of thick shoots. Only the lower part is tender enough for eating. Often found in Asian dishes.
2. Seed with the taste of black licorice; often used to flavor sweets and alcohol.
3. Root with pungent fragrance that becomes stronger when grated. Popular as a relish or a dressing for meats.
4. Plant with small, narrow leaf, often used in classic French dishes and in Béarnaise sauce. Part of a blend referred to as fines herbes.
5. Leaf of North American bush, Has a recognizable mint flavor.

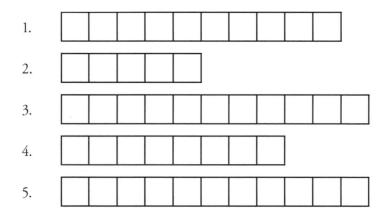

Answers on page 130

# 109

# Indian Spices

1. This hard, yellow seed is native to India. It is valued for its health properties. Taste is bitter; often used in curry powder.
2. Part of the ginger family. Scent is mild, but flavor is sharp and bitter. Often added to mustard blends. May be used as a substitute for saffron as it is similar in color and taste.
3. Powdered blend of spices adds warmth to the palate. Mixture may contain as many as 12 spices.
4. Seeds are sold whole or ground. Whole seeds are often used for pickling. Ground seeds are used to flavor baked goods. The leaves of the plant are commonly referred to as cilantro.
5. Originates from a large, fennel-like plant. Flavor is similar to garlic. Sold as a fine yellow powder or as blocks or pieces similar to gum. Used in small quantities due to its pungent flavor.

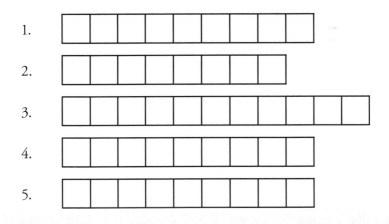

1.
2.
3.
4.
5.

Answers on page 130

# 110

# Duck

1. Name for a dish where a deboned chicken is stuffed into a deboned duck that is then stuffed into a deboned turkey.
2. City in Arkansas that holds an annual duck calling contest. This event is held around Thanksgiving.
3. Duck liver makes up this delicacy, both popular and controversial due to methods used to achieve it. French translation of this word means "fat liver."
4. Environmental factor that affects production of duck eggs. With more of this, production increases.
5. Meat from duck legs cured in salt, then marinated and poached in duck fat. French word for this means "preserved."

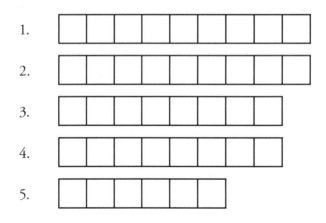

Answers on page 130

# 111

# Hershey Candy Company

1. The Hershey Co. is in this state.
2. In 1907, Hershey created this flat-bottomed milk chocolate candy with a plume at the top.
3. During World War II, Hershey created this milk chocolate bar that was named specifically for military purposes.
4. In 1938, Hershey brought out this new candy bar, initially introduced with peanuts and almonds. By the early 1940's crispy rice had replaced the nuts.
5. The first candy for Hershey originated in 1894 when Milton Hershey produced a sweet chocolate coating for what type of candy.

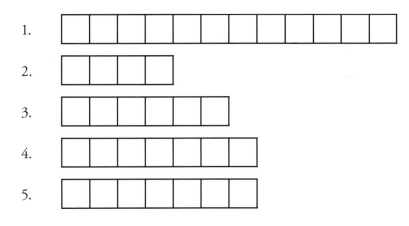

Answers on page 130

# 112

# Bitters

1. Beverages flavored with spices and what type of essence?
2. What ingredient is lacking in the production of bitters?
3. One of the best-known bitters to flavor drinks.
4. First developed in the 1800's as what type of aid?
5. Name of first bitters cocktail, created by pharmacist Antoine Amedee Peychaud, and brought to New Orleans.

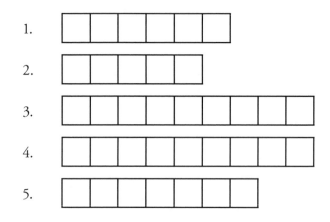

1. ☐☐☐☐☐☐

2. ☐☐☐☐☐

3. ☐☐☐☐☐☐☐☐☐☐

4. ☐☐☐☐☐☐☐☐☐

5. ☐☐☐☐☐☐☐

Answers on page 130

# 113

# Root Beer

1. Last name of the man who first sold commercial root beer to the general public.
2. One of the main ingredients in root beer comes from the oil of this root bark, originally used to make tea.
3. A popular summer dessert loved by kids and adults alike.
4. Does not naturally contain this stimulant, though it has been added to many root beer varieties.
5. This root gives root beer its characteristic frothiness.

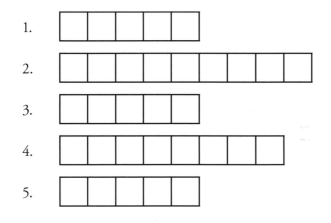

Answers on page 130

# 114

# Libations

1.  This famous tiki drink is made with rum, orange juice, Cointreau or triple sec, fresh lime juice, and orgeat syrup. This cocktail was once so popular that it was suspected to have depleted world rum supplies in the 1940's and 50's.
2.  Fashionable pink drink served in a martini glass. Can be made with a combination of vodka, Cointreau or triple sec, lime juice and a splash of cranberry juice. Popularity of this drink grew when it was served on the HBO series "Sex and The City."
3.  Originated in Cuba. Prepared with a combination of mint leaves, rum, lime, and sugar. Topped off with club soda. Similar in flavor to a mint julep.
4.  Originated in Italy and is a flavorful combination of white peach purée and prosecco. Said to have been invented in 1948 at Harry's Bar in Venice.
5.  Tropical cocktail that has a combination of rum, cream of coconut, and pine-apple juice, all blended with ice. Synonymous with the Caribbean islands.

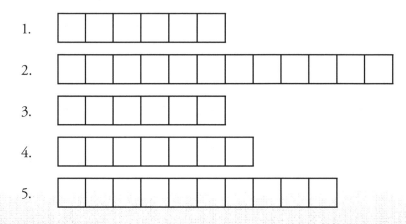

Answers on page 130

# 115

# Beer Styles

1. One of the oldest beer styles in the world. First brewed in Pilsen, Czechoslovakia, in 1842. Flavor contains hops with a hint of grain.
2. Named after the massive festival in Munich, Germany, where it is tapped for three weeks in the fall. Beer is light brown in color with a white head and has a malty character and aroma.
3. Originated in Einbeck, Germany. Bitter first taste is balanced by its sweet malt flavor.
4. Though also brewed in Chicago, most popular style is brewed in Cologne, Germany. Pale in color with a clean, refreshing flavor.
5. Belgian ale fermented with yeast and lactic acid. Taste is sour, fruity, and tart with a spritzy edge. Popular in and around Berlin, especially during the summer months. Brewed only in the German capital.

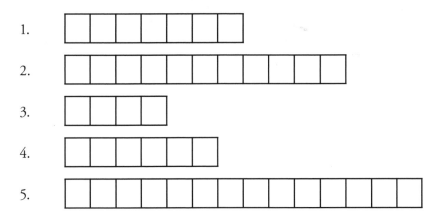

Answers on page 130

# 116

# Chinese Five Spice Powder

1. Well-known spice comes from the inner bark of a tropical evergreen tree. When dried it curls into long quills, which are either cut and sold in sticks or ground into powder. Often used in sweet dishes but lends itself well to savory dishes such as stews and curries. Very aromatic.
2. Immature, unopened bud of a tropical tree, native to Indonesia. Reddish-brown in color. Can be used whole or ground.
3. Dark brown pod of this spice contains a pea-size seed in each of its segments. Native to China, it comes from a small evergreen tree. Widely used to flavor baked goods, liqueurs, and teas.
4. Produced from the dried seeds of this aromatic plant that resembles a celery stalk with its pale green stems and green featherlike foliage. Has a mild licorice flavor.
5. A dried berry (sometimes referred to as a variety of peppercorn) from a prickly ash tree. It can be sold whole or ground into a fine powder. Associated with hot and spicy dishes from the province of China where it originated.

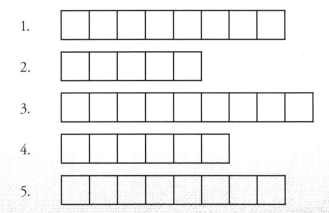

Answers on page 130

# 117

# Cloves

1. Cloves are often used to flavor this popular baked dish for holiday meals.
2. The name for clove is derived from the French word "clou" which has what meaning?
3. How many points does the bud of a clove have?
4. Cloves are cultivated from the tropical variety of this tree.
5. Cloves are used to stud this fruit for decoration during the holiday season.

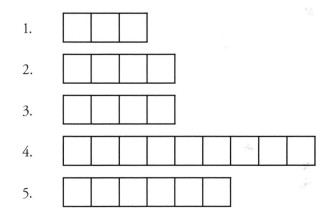

Answers on page 130

# 118

# **Wine Terms**

1. Term that indicates when a wine is not showing its full potential.
2. Description of a wine with a sharp or viscous texture caused by high glycerin levels.
3. Term describing a wine that has the aroma of fresh soil.
4. Wine with abrasive tannins or a high level of acidity.
5. Robust, full bodied wine with intense weight and flavor.

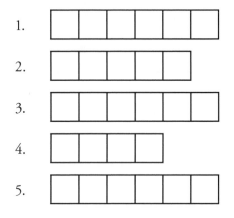

Answers on page 130

# 119

# Spanish Cheese

1. One of the most famous cheeses of Spain, produced in La Mancha and made of sheep's milk. Firm texture and zesty flavor. Rind has a zig-zag pattern.
2. Produced on the island on of Menorca. Comes in large squares weighing about 6 pounds each. Ripened in underground caves for at least 60 days. Has a salty, spicy flavor.
3. Produced in Extremadura and made of raw goat's milk. More than two-month aging period. Cheese is rubbed with a mixture of olive oil and sweet paprika. Firm enough for shaving.
4. All the milk used in production of this cheese must come from herds raised in a small zone in Northern Spain. There are blue-green veins throughout, and it has a sharp tangy flavor.
5. Produced in Galicia. Texture is elastic and creamy, with a mild, tangy flavor. Production is controlled by the Spanish government, which is only true for traditional cheeses.

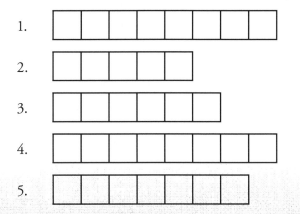

Answers on page 130

# 120

# Fresh Basil

1. In Italy, when basil is given to another person, it is a token of what?
2. Although basil is grown worldwide this country remains the principal source followed by the United States.
3. Basil leaves are combined with garlic, pine nuts, olive oil, and fresh grated parmesan cheese to make this popular pasta sauce.
4. Basil is an excellent source of this fat-soluble vitamin. It is necessary for normal blood clotting and for making bone proteins.
5. Thai basil has a pungent yet sweet smell and has a flavor similar to what licorice flavored herbaceous plant?

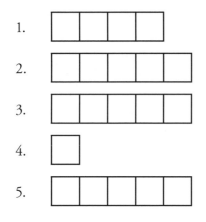

Answers on page 130

# 121

# Bacon 101

1. 70 percent of bacon is consumed at what meal?
2. In England, a slice of bacon is known as what?
3. International bacon day is held annually on the Saturday before what U.S. holiday?
4. Provides the most flavor in bacon.
5. Bacon is made from fresh pork and goes through what process of preservation with salt to ensure that it will keep longer? There are two methods for this: dry and wet.

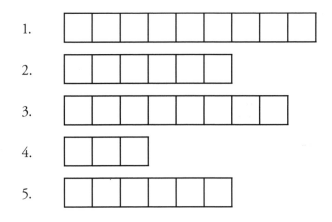

Answers on page 130

# 122

# Food Themed Movies

1. The story chronicles the lives of two Italian brothers whose restaurant is on the verge of bankruptcy. They risk everything on an extravagant feast for a popular band leader. Made in 1978. Stanley Tucci stars in this movie.
2. A single mother and daughter move to rural France to open a chocolate shop. They meet with resistance until people taste their delicious creations. Cast includes Juliette Binoche, Judi Dench and Johnny Depp. Made in 2000.
3. The star of this Pixar film is Remy, a food obsessed rat who lives in France and ends up creating delicious food with a young kitchen worker in a Paris restaurant. It was made in 2007.
4. Sunday dinners at Mother Joe's have a wonderful 40-year tradition. When bickering starts to tear the family apart, Ahmad, the grandson, works to get the family back together and teach them the true meaning of love, family, and food. Stars Irma P. Hall, Vanessa Williams and Nia Long. Made in 1997.
5. Jack Nicholson stars in one of the most memorable scenes filmed in a roadside diner. Made in 1970.

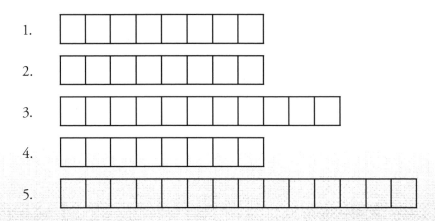

Answers on page 130

# 123

# Food Lyrics

1. Prince sings about working in the five and dime. This song title uses the name of a well-known red fruit and a popular type of French hat.
2. Sung by the Beatles: "A place where nothing is real and there is nothing to get hung up about." These fields are forever.
3. Sung by UB40. Makes you feel so fine and keeps you rocking all the time. "Red, Red…."
4. Neil Young sings about a special girl, referring to a popular spice that is reddish-brown in color.
5. Jimmy Buffet sings about amending his carnivorous habits and eating this in paradise.

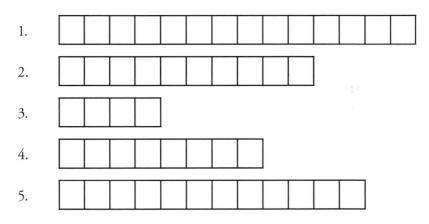

Answers on page 130

# 124

# Berries

1. What is the most popular berry in the U.S. in terms of cultivation and consumption?
2. Early American colonists made grey paint by boiling what dark colored berry in milk?
3. Similar in shape to raspberries but larger in size and a much darker color.
4. Rudolph B. is believed to be the inventor of this berry. He experimented with a variety of berry crosses in Napa Valley in the 1920's. The preserves produced from this berry helped put Knott's business on the map.
5. An uncultivated member of the cranberry family. Mostly used in Europe in the production of jams and jellies. Also, a member of the foxberry and cowberry family.

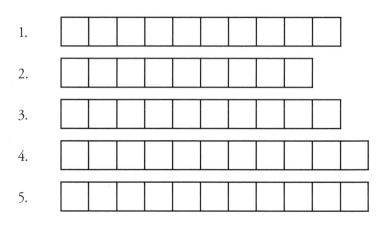

Answers on page 130

# 125

# Grapes

1. Name for the dried version of a grape. This is a popular snack food, especially for kids.
2. Grapes are a healthy, low calorie food choice. They are made up of eighty percent of what essential liquid/element?
3. A large, plump grape that is purplish-red in color. This variety is used primarily to produce juice and wine.
4. The two most popular varieties of grape are American and what?
5. Two thirds of the grapes grown in the U.S. are grown in this state.

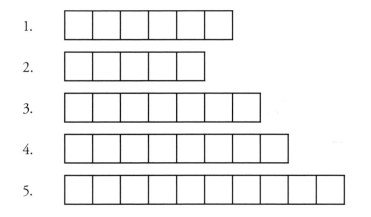

Answers on page 130

# Eat Your Words Puzzle Book Answers

| | | | | | |
|---|---|---|---|---|---|
| Sausage | p.1 | 1. andouille | 2. bratwurst | 3. Italian | 4. kielbasa | 5. pepperoni |
| Squash | p.2 | 1. hubbard | 2. kabocha | 3. calabash | 4. acorn | 5. delicata |
| Nuts | p.3 | 1. macadamia | 2. pistachio | 3. pine | 4. chestnut | 5. cashew |
| Sauces | p.4 | 1. béarnaise | 2. béchamel | 3. bordelaise | 4. aioli | 5. velouté |
| Sugar | p.5 | 1. powdered | 2. sanding | 3. turbinado | 4. muscovado | 5. demerara |
| Flour | p.6 | 1. semolina | 2. pastry | 3. bread | 4. instant | 5. soy |
| Stone Fruits | p.7 | 1. apricot | 2. peach | 3. cherry | 4. plum | 5. nectarine |
| Olives | p.8 | 1. manzanilla | 2. kalamata | 3. niçoise | 4. mission | 5. brining |
| Taste of Japan | p.9 | 1. sake | 2. sushi | 3. udon | 4. tempura | 5. omurice |
| Mushrooms | p.10 | 1. chanterelle | 2. shiitake | 3. oyster | 4. morel | 5. portobello |
| Taste of Mexico | p.11 | 1. chilorio | 2. quesadilla | 3. frijol pinto | 4. enchilada | 5. pico de gallo |
| Hungarian Cuisine | p.12 | 1. goulash | 2. palinka | 3. strudel | 4. paprika | 5. dobos torte |
| Taste of Sicily | p.13 | 1. caponata | 2. cannoli | 3. pecorino | 4. gelato | 5. marsala |
| Tropical Fruits | p.14 | 1. cherimoya | 2. guava | 3. jackfruit | 4. plantain | 5. passion fruit |
| French Terms | p.15 | 1. amuse bouche | 2. bon appétit | 3. apéritif | 4. brioche | 5. gratin |
| Mangoes | p.16 | 1. India | 2. orange | 3. A | 4. amchoor | 5. haden |
| Citrus | p.17 | 1. orange | 2. lime | 3. kumquat | 4. bergamot | 5. yuzu |
| Taste of China | p.18 | 1. peking | 2. congee | 3. wonton | 4. dim sum | 5. hot pot |
| Taste of Australia | p.19 | 1. damper | 2. pavlova | 3. kangaroo | 4. yabby | 5. vegemite |
| World of Dumplings | p.20 | 1. gnocchi | 2. pierogi | 3. späetzle | 4. pot sticker | 5. mandu |
| Taste of Greece | p.21 | 1. feta | 2. pastitsio | 3. baklava | 4. ouzo | 5. saganaki |
| Tea | p.22 | 1. assam | 2. oolong | 3. Early Grey | 4. Jasmine | 5. chai |
| Taste of Germany | p.23 | 1. späetzle | 2. hasenpfeffer | 3. sauerkraut | 4. sauerbraten | 5. Jägermeister |
| Let's Talk Turkey | p.24 | 1. Tom | 2. hen | 3. gizzard | 4. beard | 5. wishbone |
| Pumpkins | p.25 | 1. water | 2. pies | 3. potassium | 4. freckles | 5. beta carotene |
| Taste of Morocco | p.26 | 1. tagine | 2. couscous | 3. mechoui | 4. bisteeya | 5. mhalbi |
| Taste of Nicaragua | p.27 | 1. quesillo | 2. tres leches | 3. gallo pinto | 4. picante | 5. platano |
| Southern Food | p.28 | 1. cracklings | 2. oxtail | 3. succotash | 4. hush puppy | 5. grits |
| Taste of Mexico II | p.29 | 1. bolillo | 2. carne | 3. cilantro | 4. masa | 5. queso |

128

| | | | | | |
|---|---|---|---|---|---|
| Bread | p.69 | 1. babka | 2. bolillo | 3. ciabatta | 4. sugar | 5. flour |
| Waffles | p.70 | 1. Belgium | 2. wafel | 3. eggo | 4. baking soda | 5. waffle iron |
| Chocolate | p.71 | 1. couverture | 2. bittersweet | 3. milk chocolate | 4. bloom | 5. temper |
| Top Chef Trivia | p.72 | 1. quickfire | 2. food and wine | 3. Tom Colicchio | 4. Padma | 5. knives |
| Taste of Ireland | p.73 | 1. boxty | 2. coddle | 3. barmbrack | 4. Guinness | 5. Irish coffee |
| Cooking Techniques | p.74 | 1. blanch | 2. purée | 3. reduce | 4. baste | 5. degrease |
| Pastry Tools | p.75 | 1. blender | 2. brush | 3. scraper | 4. sock | 5. bag |
| Champagne | p.76 | 1. brut | 2. cuvée | 3. rosé | 4. demi sec | 5. France |
| Steak Dishes | p.77 | 1. au poivre | 2. Diane | 3. tartare | 4. Swiss | 5. salisbury |
| Cookies of the Globe | p.78 | 1. linzer | 2. pizzelle | 3. rosette | 4. letterbanket | 5. tuile |
| Cracker Jacks | p.79 | 1. molasses | 2. prize | 3. Frito Lay | 4. Sailor Jack | 5. seventh |
| Chef's Tools | p.80 | 1. skimmer | 2. microplane | 3. mandoline | 4. sifter | 5. serrated |
| Grill Types | p.81 | 1. hibachi | 2. kettle | 3. electric | 4. smoker | 5. gas |
| Candy Corn | p.82 | 1. honey | 2. corn kernel | 3. yellow | 4. 70 | 5. Brach's |
| Sweet Treats | p.83 | 1. coulis | 2. essence | 3. panna cotta | 4. Napoleon | 5. granita |
| Cookware | p.84 | 1. teflon | 2. cast iron | 3. aluminum | 4. copper | 5. stainless |
| Taste of New Orleans | p.85 | 1. po' boy | 2. beignet | 3. jambalaya | 4. gumbo | 5. muffuletta |
| Honey | p.86 | 1. nectar | 2. six | 3. wax | 4. glucose | 5. apiarist |
| Anatomy of a Cookie | p.87 | 1. fat | 2. egg | 3. leavening | 4. sugar | 5. flour |
| Baklava | p.88 | 1. Greece | 2. phyllo | 3. triangle | 4. nuts | 5. honey |
| Italian Desserts | p.89 | 1. affogato | 2. amaretti | 3. zabaglione | 4. spumoni | 5. panettone |
| Salmon | p.90 | 1. king | 2. sockeye | 3. coho | 4. chum | 5. Copper River |
| Wine Bottles | p.91 | 1. split | 2. magnum | 3. Jeroboam | 4. Balthazar | 5. Salmanazar |
| Game Birds | p.92 | 1. pheasant | 2. quail | 3. goose | 4. grouse | 5. turkey |
| Julia Child | p.93 | 1. Smith | 2. Cambridge | 3. Le Cordon Bleu | 4. Jacques Pepin | 5. tall |
| Meringue | p.94 | 1. white | 2. tartar | 3. humidity | 4. peaks | 5. yolk |
| State Fair Foods | p.95 | 1. pronto pup | 2. funnel | 3. cheese curd | 4. onion | 5. mini doughnuts |
| Wraps | p.96 | 1. bamboo | 2. banana | 3. grape | 4. gyoza | 5. lumpia |
| Bourbon | p.97 | 1. whiskey | 2. aging | 3. corn | 4. Bardstown | 5. Manhattan |
| Beer | p.98 | 1. Pabst | 2. Anheuser Busch | 3. Molson | 4. Heineken | 5. Guinness |
| Sourdough | p.99 | 1. Egypt | 2. gluten | 3. starter | 4. San Francisco | 5. Boule |
| Sauces | p.100 | 1. Alfredo | 2. chimichurri | 3. cocktail | 4. romesco | 5. Newburg |
| Oats | p.101 | 1. rolled | 2. quick | 3. instant | 4. flour | 5. bran |
| Almonds | p.102 | 1. bee | 2. 1,000 | 3. Jordan | 4. stone | 5. chocolate |
| Vanilla | p.103 | 1. vanillan | 2. paste | 3. powder | 4. pure | 5. Madagascar |
| International Drinks | p.104 | 1. Limoncello | 2. frappé | 3. eggnog | 4. lassi | 5. coquito |
| Irish Whiskey | p.105 | 1. three | 2. wooden | 3. single malt | 4. mash | 5. Bushmills |

| | | | | | |
|---|---|---|---|---|---|
| Candy Canes | p.106 | 1. white | 2. Germany | 3. peppermint | 4. red | 5. tree |
| Vegetarian Options | p.107 | 1. pollotarian | 2. lacto-ovo | 3. flexitarian | 4. pescatarian | 5. ovo |
| Flavorful Plants | p.108 | 1. lemongrass | 2. anise | 3. horseradish | 4. tarragon | 5. wintergreen |
| Indian Spices | p.109 | 1. fenugreek | 2. turmeric | 3. garam masala | 4. coriander | 5. asafetida |
| Duck | p.110 | 1. Turducken | 2. Stuttgart | 3. foie gras | 4. daylight | 5. confit |
| Hershey Candy Company | p.111 | 1. Pennsylvania | 2. kiss | 3. ration | 4. krackel | 5. caramel |
| Bitters | p.112 | 1. herbal | 2. sugar | 3. angostura | 4. digestive | 5. sazerac |
| Root Beer | p.113 | 1. Hires | 2. sassafras | 3. float | 4. caffeine | 5. yucca |
| Libations | p.114 | 1. mai tai | 2. cosmopolitan | 3. mojito | 4. bellini | 5. pina colada |
| Beer Styles | p.115 | 1. pilsner | 2. Oktoberfest | 3. bock | 4. kolsch | 5. Berliner weisse |
| Chinese Five Spice Powder | p.116 | 1. cinnamon | 2. clove | 3. star anise | 4. fennel | 5. Szechuan |
| Cloves | p.117 | 1. ham | 2. nail | 3. four | 4. evergreen | 5. orange |
| Wine Terms | p.118 | 1. closed | 2. chewy | 3. earthy | 4. hard | 5. brawny |
| Spanish Cheeses | p.119 | 1. Manchego | 2. Mahon | 3. Ibores | 4. Cabrales | 5. Tetilla |
| Fresh Basil | p.120 | 1. love | 2. Egypt | 3. pesto | 4. K | 5. anise |
| Bacon 101 | p.121 | 1. breakfast | 2. rasher | 3. Labor Day | 4. fat | 5. curing |
| Food Themed Movies | p.122 | 1. Big Night | 2. Chocolat | 3. Ratatouille | 4. Soul food | 5. Five easy pieces |
| Music with Food in The Lyrics | p.123 | 1. Raspberry beret | 2. strawberry | 3. wine | 4. cinnamon | 5. cheeseburger |
| Berries | p.124 | 1. strawberry | 2. blueberry | 3. blackberry | 4. boysenberry | 5. lingonberry |
| Grapes | p.125 | 1. raisin | 2. Water | 3. Catawba | 4. European | 5. California |

# About The Author

Lisa Patrin is a recipe creator, food writer, and the author of The Empty Nesters Kitchen blog. Lisa is passionate about promoting local food producers and she is a food justice & sustainability advocate. Follow Lisa's blog at www.emptynesterskitchen.com and her travel and culinary journeys on Instagram at emptynesterskitchen and on Twitter at lpatrin

Made in United States
Orlando, FL
08 December 2021

11295466R00088